Peter Corris is a former academic turned journalist, thriller writer and jogger.

Born in Victoria, he is now an enthusiastic resident of Sydney, which has provided the inspiration and locale for his other Cliff Hardy stories – *The Dying Trade, White Meat, The Marvellous Boy, Heroin Annie and Make Me Rich*. He is also the author of *The Winning Side*, a compelling novel about a part-Aboriginal boxer who becomes a journalist, and his fight for equality and respect.

'Most of all there is the tang, often the sour tang, of inner Sydney, the hot and humid streets which may be corrupt but are never mean.'

Sydney Morning Herald

BY THE SAME AUTHOR
The Dying Trade
White Meat
The Marvellous Boy

THE EMPTY BEACH

Peter Corris

UNWIN PAPERBACKS
Sydney   London   Boston

For Heidi von Born

First published in Australia
by Unwin Paperbacks 1983
Reprinted 1984, 1985

UNWIN® PAPERBACKS
George Allen & Unwin Australia Pty Ltd
8 Napier St, North Sydney, NSW 2060, Australia

UNWIN PAPERBACKS
18 Park Lane, Hemel Hempstead,
Herts HP2 4TE, England

© Peter Corris 1983

National Library of Australia
Cataloguing-in-Publication entry:
Corris, Peter, 1942–
The empty beach
ISBN 0 86861 229 4
1. Title.
A 823'

Published with the assistance of the Literature Board
of the Australia Council.
Set in Century 9/11 by B & D Modgraphic
Printed by The Dominion Press-Hedges & Ball
Maryborough, 3465

1

SHE gave me instructions to meet her in the lounge of the Regal hotel and, while I haven't been shy about going into hotels for the past twenty-odd years, today I was just a bit reluctant. It was close to three pm on a fine day with low pollution levels; my own pollution level was low too, because it was two months and sixteen days since I'd stopped smoking. But now I wanted a cigarette badly. I'd been a private detective for ten years, near enough, and I'd always had a cigarette before I met a client, several while I talked and listened, and a few more afterwards while I thought. It was a hard pattern to break.

The Regal dominates a stretch of the Parade at Bondi; it's white, of course, with a few turrets, one of which supports a flagpole and flag. The palm trees on either side of the entrance would go better in Singapore, but they're doing their best. I was early as always and I wandered down to the beach to kill the time. The suntanned people outnumbered the pallid, although it was only October. You can sunbathe all the year round in Sydney if you pick your spots and days and have nothing better to do.

I stood on the steps of the pavilion looking out at the heavy surf and the few people braving it with their boards and bodies. They looked frail, as if the sea was playing with them rather than the other way around. Any minute, it seemed, the water could rise up and obliterate them. But the sun was shining and the sand glowed; some of the pale people were turning pink and it was no time for glum thoughts. I took two lungfuls of the ozone and still wanted a cigarette.

The lounge of the Regal was dark and quiet, as lounges should be, and I had to peer about before I located the woman at a table in the corner. As I went across I thought that this was a good place to arrange a meeting—she would have a chance to see her man irresolute before he saw her. My client would have seen a tall, thin man, dark and not saved from looking forty by the soft light. She sat straight and square-shouldered in her chair and held out her hand. Businesslike.

'Mr Hardy.'

'Mrs Singer.' Her grip was dry and firm. It was a nice hand to shake.

'Marion,' she said. 'I'm the client, I'll buy the drinks. I was having a gin and tonic.'

'I'll have the same. Thanks.'

She raised her hand and a waiter came over to take the order. I guessed her age at about fifty, perhaps a bit more, but the few extra years weren't showing. She wore a blue linen suit with a white blouse. Her hair was somewhere between blonde and grey and it suited her strong-featured face. She had big eyes, brown, a curved nose and one of those mouths that seems to have a line drawn around it, defining it. As I feared, she was smoking. Her brand was Kent, though, which wasn't too hard to resist.

'What do you think of Bondi?' It wasn't a question I'd expected, so for the second time she had the advantage of me.

'I like it,' I said. 'I'm proud of it.'

She smiled at me and gave a bit of the smile to the waiter. She stubbed out her Kent and drank some gin.

'What do you know about me, Mr Hardy?'

I took a short pull on the drink. 'Married to John Singer,' I said. 'Sorry, that might be offensive, talking about you in terms of your husband. Habit. I don't know anything about you, Mrs Singer, except that you phoned me up this morning, mentioned an old client of mine and arranged this meeting.'

She laughed. 'I'm not offended. I'm proud to have been married to John. What do you know about him, then?'

'John Singer disappeared from Bondi beach about two years ago.' I swung around and pointed to one of the big, shaded windows. 'Out there. He was a businessman, successful. Bit of a black marketeer just after the war, then involved with vending machines, pinballs after that. He had interests in taxis and

2

hotels, probably other things too, but the pinballs were the hard core at the end.'

'That's a funny way of putting it,' she said. 'Are you against pinball machines?'

I shrugged, drank some more gin and wished her cigarette smoke would blow the other way. She'd lit that one while she was talking, the way an experienced smoker can.

'Not particularly,' I said. 'Mindless stuff. Profitable, I suppose. I wish the kids were spending their time better.'

'Not only kids. Adults, too.'

'They're a lost cause. Retards.'

She laughed again. 'Well, you've got it pretty right. I'm impressed that you learned so much so fast. I keep the business going as best I can.'

I nodded. She was buying the drinks; she could do the talking.

'You must be curious about this meeting?'

'Very.'

'John may not be dead.'

I nodded, sceptically this time. Harold Holt might not be dead and Sean Flynn and a few thousand others who probably were. You get a lot of nuts in this business, fantasists. I was suddenly feeling less curious about the meeting and I let it show. She leaned forward across the props of alcohol and tobacco and spoke urgently, with strong need in her voice.

'A week ago I got a phone call. He said he saw John in Roscoe Street, shabby and sick.'

'He?'

'A man's voice. That's all he said. Wait, I wrote it down.' She fished up a leather bag from somewhere, rummaged in it and came up with a sheet of notepaper. She passed it across. The message was written in capitals: 'I SAW JOHN IN ROSCOE STREET MRS SINGER. HE LOOKS CROOK.'

'Not eloquent,' I said.

'No, but a big shock. I want you to check into it, of course. See if there's anything in it.'

'You didn't know the voice?'

'No. It wasn't a nice voice. Very harsh.'

'Young or old?'

'Oh, old, I'd say.'

'This was a week ago, you say. You've been thinking about it. Is it all right to ask you how you want it to turn out—dead or alive, as it were?' I'd picked up her book matches, pulled two out and was shredding them with my fingers, all without knowing it. She tapped my hand with two fingers that carried pricey-looking rings.

'Stop fidgeting. Why are you doing that?'

'I stopped smoking.'

'You poor bastard. Why?'

'To slow down the ageing process.'

'You're ageing all right, I've seen worse. Another drink?'

'I'm watching that, too. No, thanks. What about it, Marion? Dead or alive?'

She finished her drink and pushed it aside as if my example had given her strength, but she didn't have the skin of a boozer.

'I'm not sure,' she said slowly. 'I'd adjusted, got used to the idea. I'll be frank. I suppose I hope it's not true. John and I had been married for fifteen years. We weren't love birds any more.'

'Any children?'

She tapped another Kent out, another little reward or penance. 'No.'

'Would he have had any reason to fake a disappearance? You know, like that Pommy politician?'

'Stonehouse,' she said automatically. 'Not that I can think of.'

'Up till you got this call, what did you think had happened to him?'

'He suicided, it was an accident or he was murdered. I just don't know.'

'What would you bet?'

'I don't know,' she repeated. 'Look, we weren't all that close at the end. John had other women and I had other men. But we got along all right and the business was in good shape when I took it over. He could have had worries. He was a secretive man.'

4

'It sounds as if you didn't know a lot about him.'

'Well, it was like that. John was an Englishman, came here after the war. I'm a Kiwi myself. I left New Zealand in 1950 and I've never been back. We both loved Sydney, Bondi particularly. No ties for either of us. We both worked at the business and played a lot of tennis and golf. We had a lovely boat. It was enough.'

Just great, Cliff, I thought. *Canny Pom goes missing off the beach, wife grieves mildly because she doesn't know him all that well.* It sounded like two days on the street, two hundred dollars and lunch money. Still, maybe I could get some swimming in. I told her I'd do what I could and she wrote me a cheque. I noticed she didn't write my name on the stub.

'I'll need a photograph,' I said.

'Oh yes. I've got one here of John on the yacht. He's got a few days growth, but . . .' She dug in the bag, which rustled and clinked the way women's bags do. 'Damn! I thought I had it.'

'I suppose I could get a newspaper photo.'

'You'd be lucky. John didn't go in for publicity.' She looked at her digital watch. 'I wanted to meet you here because it's quiet and I didn't want to broadcast my business. My flat's a bit public.' She put her cigarettes and matches away. 'But I feel a bit better just from talking about it.'

She pulled out her purse and a sheet of typing paper came out with it. She looked at it like an actress studying her lines. 'Here's a list of some of John's interests, the places where he spent some time. It might help.'

I took the paper and she put money on the table.

'Run me home,' she said. 'I'll get the photo.'

I escorted her out to my Falcon with a touch of pride. My last case but one had been a moderately fat job and I'd had some money to spend on the car—mechanical overhaul, paint, fresh upholstery in the front. The last case was better forgotten, a foul-up that had cost me money. All the more reason to open the car door smartly for Mrs Marion Singer and not to shut it too roughly after she'd glided her nice, neat legs inside. It costs nothing to be a gentleman, as old Jack Dempsey used to say.

5

She directed me north up the hill and around a couple of turns that brought me out in a street I didn't know. It ran along the side of a cliff that dropped away down to water, rocks and a little sand. There were four apartment blocks. Chez Singer was in a ten-storey block that boasted the name The Reefs. None of the residents would be victims of life's shipwrecks. The building soared up and was placed to give a maximum view of the water; the balconies were long and deep and the acres of glass were tinted. I guessed that a title for one of the apartments would change hands for around a quarter of a million. I steered the Falcon towards a car park with more potted plants than Vaucluse House. Mrs Singer turned, looked out the back window and prodded my arm.

'Bugger it,' she said. 'Mac's here. Stop a bit further on.'

I drove past the entrance to the car park, rolling gently. 'Who's Mac?'

'My business partner, sort of,' she said. 'I'll mail you the photo. Sorry.' She clutched at her bag, nervously I thought. 'I'll have to think of some story if he saw you.'

'You could say I was your long-lost cousin from New Zealand.'

'God forbid. Please do your best, Mr Hardy, and keep me informed.'

She got out and walked back to The Reefs. She walked well, head up, tummy in, as befitted someone who filled in her time with tennis and golf. I drove on to the end of the street, past The Main, turned and came back. Through the entrance I saw Mrs Singer talking to a man who stood with one hand almost possessively on her arm. I stopped and looked at them among the potted palms. He was stout, no taller than she, and built wide, like an all-in wrestler.

2

'Hey!' The call came from the other side of the street and a little behind me. It came from a car, not an ordinary car like a Bentley or a Saab, but from a silver Cadillac. Why I hadn't spotted it until then I don't know. With its gleaming chrome and tinted glass it was like a peacock in a chookyard.

A thin white arm reached out of the window in the front of the car and on the road side. It beckoned to me and I got out and went across to it and the car. The Cadillac was like one of the old, Gothic models that had been put on a diet. It was lower and sleeker but a longish walk would still be required to get round it. It carried cheeky gold and blue Californian number plates with the New South Wales plates mounted above them. The customised plate was MAC 1.

The arm belonged to a blonde. She had makeup in every place it could be applied and her almost white hair was curled and twisted in ways that cost money. She put a cigarette in her mouth and narrowed her eyes. At a distance, she'd have passed for eighteen, up close she looked as if she should be in the third form somewhere doing domestic science.

'Can you give me a light, please?'

I shook my head. 'You're too young to smoke.'

'I'm too young to do a lot of things,' she giggled. 'Doesn't stop me.'

I glanced back towards The Reefs. The wrestler was laying down the law to my client but she shook her head and puffed smoke and didn't seem concerned. The blonde didn't like being looked away from.

'Hey, are you sure you haven't got a match?'

'I'm sure,' I said. 'There'll be a lighter on that flight deck somewhere.'

She shook her head. 'There's so many switches, and Mac won't ever leave me the keys. He's afraid I'll just drive away.'

'Can you manage a left-hand drive?'

'Huh?'

'Never mind. What's Mac's game? Hamburgers?'

She laughed. It was a sound she hadn't worked on unlike her voice, which was stage-throaty. The laugh was clear and girlish and suddenly it all felt sad and smutty—the schoolgirl with the cigarette in the big, arrogant car. She was wearing a pink top and tiny shorts, spike heels and a thin gold chain around her right ankle. She saw me looking and poked her tongue out between her little white teeth.

'You're in trouble,' she purred. 'Here comes Bob.'

I swung around to see a big man moving fast around the back of the car and coming towards me. I stepped away from the Caddy and heard the blonde giggle again.

'On your way, mister,' Bob said. He was six foot three and under the tight tennis shirt he had wide shoulders and a flat middle.

'Just chatting,' I said.

'He said he wanted to fuck me,' the blonde said. 'He said he wanted to suck my tits.'

I felt a small wave of panic rising. Bob looked like just the sort of boy you'd hire to stamp out unwanted tit-sucking. He kept his hands low and put his back gently against the car. It was a good position in which to duck or from which to launch an attack. Bob knew his business and I just wanted to mind mine.

'The lady's overwrought,' I said. 'She reads too much.'

'That little twat can't read,' he said. 'And you'd need the mouthwash handy if you were going to suck her.'

'He wanted to show me his dick,' the blonde chirped.

'If he did, you wouldn't know whether to lie down or open your mouth.'

'You're a shit, Bob. I know what you want.'

He sighed. 'I want to keep Mac happy and draw my pay. That means keeping sluts like you unbruised. You won't be the last,

Sharon.'

'Look,' I said, 'it's been exciting talking to you, but I think I'll be going.'

'You do that.' He rubbed against the car like a cat. 'I'm a bit disappointed. Thought you might have a go.'

Sharon wriggled in her moulded bucket seat and pulled her top down an inch.

'Get rid of him, Bob,' she hissed. 'Mac's coming.'

I turned and saw the bull-like man heading towards us with his head down and his shoulders hunched. He kicked savagely at a can in his way and it screeched and clattered across the concrete.

Bob had straightened up like a guardsman awaiting inspection. I grinned at him. 'Another time,' I said. I backed across to my car, got in and drove away before Mac made it out to the street. In the rear vision mirror I saw Bob pull open the kerbside door so that Mac could settle in behind the left hand drive steering wheel.

3

M Y habit is to run a good check on the client before pounding the pavement and knocking on doors, otherwise a man could end up working for a white slaver or a politician. The little I had on Singer was from one source only—a friend in the credit rating racket. I needed more, so I called Harry Tickener at the *News* and got temporary researcher status, which admitted me to the paper's first-class library.

Mrs Singer had been right about John's penchant for the low profile. The newspapers had reported as fully as they could on his disappearance, but they were scratching to fill the space when it came to background dope. He had extensive business interests concentrated in the eastern suburbs of Sydney, was fifty-eight years of age and president of his tennis club. That last piece of data showed how hard up the papers had been for copy.

There was no photograph of him. I read the reports carefully. Singer had been in the habit of jogging along the roads at first light (not down on the sand, where you couldn't move for seekers after aerobic fitness). He'd gone for his run early on a bleak August morning and that had been the last anyone had seen of him. A towelling headband he always wore had been washed up on the beach later the following day, and that was it.

My client hadn't rated a mention in the papers at all; she hadn't been seen anywhere wearing anything, hadn't put flowers around the necks of racehorses or danced with the premier. My jottings from these stunning pieces of journalism hardly filled half a sheet of notebook paper.

I found Harry Tickener belting his typewriter in his latest attempt to win the elusive Walkley Award. Harry has filled out a bit over the years, but his mind is still lean and sharp. I tried the name Singer on him.

'Nope,' he said. He stared down at his copy paper as if he might forget forever the next thing he wanted to say. 'Never heard anything about him. Try Garth.'

'Thanks, Harry.'

He waved a hand, but already had the other on the keys, chasing the Walkley. Harry will spend a week drinking and going to the races when it suits him, but when he works he works.

Garth Green is known as 'the bear' because he's big and brown and sprouts hair everywhere. He lost his struggle against the cigarette habit and coughs happily along, quoting John O'Hara: 'When I first lit and inhaled a cigarette I knew I was not taking a Horlicks malted milk tablet.' I wish I could see it like that. We exchanged the usual insults and I named my man.

'Singer ... Singer.' He sucked on his cigarette and drew the smoke down to his boots. 'I heard a bit about him before he went for his dip. A Brit, wasn't he? Word was he was an ex-commando and as tough as they come. He had to be to make a go of it in the game he was in.'

'No whispers? Slow gee gees, little girls, little boys?'

'You've got a filthy mind, Cliff. No, not a thing. He ran a solid operation in the eastern suburbs. Tom McLeary has a big part of it and someone else whose name eludes me. Mac's a tough guy, too.'

'Mac?' I said. 'Would he be a shortish character, built like a bull?'

'That's him. Not a nice bloke, but he hasn't killed anyone recently that I know of. Famous for his bad temper. He's exploded in public a couple of times and made some lawyers and dentists rich.'

'How did he and Singer get on?'

'Don't know. Uneasily, I'd guess. What's the story?'

'Off the record. Someone thinks he might be still alive. I'm sniffing at it.'

A great gust of coughing swept Garth up, doubled him over and left him gripping the edge of the desk.

'Jesus,' I said, 'I thought I was going to see a lung.'

'No lungs left.' He lit another cigarette and blew smoke at me.

11

'How crooked was Singer, Garth?'

'Hard to say. Fifty per cent might be right. Some pretty heavy people running things out there, Cliff. You want to watch your step.'

I thumped my chest. 'I don't smoke. My wind is sound. I'll run away.'

It was late in the afternoon and the city traffic was thickening fast. I decided to have a drink while it eased off and then potter around in Bondi for a bit to get the feel of the place. On the off chance, I stuck my head in at the photo room, where they have a thousand pictures of Sophia Loren and one of Bertrand Russell, if you're lucky. It's heavily protected territory, out of bounds to all but the properly accredited. Most of the minions enforce the rules but Thelma Clark doesn't, and she was there when I called in.

'S for Singer,' I said.

'I can't hear you,' she said. 'I can't see you. Along the right-hand wall and you've got twenty seconds.'

I slid in, slithered along the wall and grabbed the box that contained the photographic likenesses of people from Silverman to Sixtus. Marion Singer had been wrong; there was a picture of Singer talking to a judge of the licensing court who was obviously the main subject of the shot. Someone had bothered to tag Singer, too, so he achieved immortality. The judge was pretty well known, so I went over my twenty seconds and looked in his box as well. There were three copies of the photo which did not name Singer. I slipped one of them into my pocket. Thelma didn't even look up as I went out.

I walked to a pub where they leave the lights on in the saloon bar so you can see what you're drinking. I bought a scotch and a packet of chips and sat down to study the picture.

It's hard to tell in photographs when you don't have a point of reference, and the judge could have been Alan Ladd-sized for all I knew, but Singer looked big. I'd put him at around six feet two with a strong build; he had a large, slightly meaty face with wavy fair hair. He looked a little like Michael Caine, the English actor. I drank and munched chips and decided that he looked a *lot* like Caine. That made it instantly impossible to assign any characteristics to him; I thought of Caine in *Alfie* and *The Eagle Has Landed* and Singer took on some of that role-switching insubstantiality. I put the picture away and had another drink and thought that an Englishman that big with a face like that shouldn't be too hard to spot, even if he was looking crook.

I'd been wearing slacks with shoes and white shirt for my meeting with the widow Singer. Very square and all wrong for Bondi of a spring evening, so I drove home to Glebe to change. Things have looked up at home since I took in a tenant. The newspapers, delivered while I've been away on high-powered forty-eight-hour surveillance jobs, and the green plastic garbage bags, symbols of collections missed, haven't built up in the front garden. Hildegarde is twenty-two, a final year dentistry student. She answered an advertisement I put in the local paper for a lodger. She was the brightest-looking applicant, and she told me that she had no unsavoury habits or hobbies. She smiled when she said that and then told me she played tennis a lot. That was good enough for me.

She was making coffee when I went in. I had a lightning-fast shave, put on jeans and a T-shirt and came through, sniffing the coffee aroma. Hilde poured me one.

'Going out?'

'Yep, Bondi.' I sipped the coffee, which was better than I've ever been able to make.

'A yacht party?'

'There's no yachts at Bondi, you ignorant Balt.'

Hilde has a clean German skin and long, pale hair which she ties back or lets loose, according to her mood. We've been close to going to bed together a couple of times, but haven't quite got there. I doubt that we will now, although then a long celibacy was nagging me. She's too independent, I'm too mistrustful. We play tennis occasionally and she beats me.

She drank the coffee scalding, the way she can.

'Bondi,' she said, 'let's see. Surf. You don't surf. Rock music. You don't need it. I don't know anything else about the place, except it's got a lot of New Zealanders. Do you speak New Zealand?'

'Sure. Pakeha, Waikato. I'm working, love. What'll you do tonight?'

'Study,' she said. 'Root canals.'

I shuddered and blew on the coffee. 'Torturers all.'

She grinned at me. 'I need to practise. How about a session in the chair?'

'Get out of my house. Any mail?'

She pointed to a few envelopes beside the bread box, and I poked at them without interest. I took the picture of Singer from my hip pocket and passed it across the table.

'What d'you make of him? Would he need the novocaine?'

She studied the picture. 'No chance. A real tough guy.' She frowned. 'He looks like someone I know.'

I sighed. 'Michael Caine.'

'That's right! I loved him as the good Nazi.' She gave me a challenging look across her cup. Her people left Germany sometime in the 1920s and went to Palestine to grow olives. They were interned by the British and put on ships going here and there. The Stōners ended up in Australia and became Stones. Hilde's an anarchist freethinker, but she likes to play the Hun.

'He was great,' I said. 'But this isn't him. This bloke could mean big money for me if I find him ... or if I don't.'

'I don't understand.'

'Neither do I. Well, I'm off to Bondi. Thanks for the coffee.'

'Aren't you going to eat?'

'What do they eat in Bondi, do you reckon?'

She shrugged. 'Dunno. Fish and chips, I suppose.'

'Lovely.'

I reclaimed the picture, checked that I had some business cards and money and set out for Bondi where Sir Charles Kingsford Smith nearly got drowned and where John Singer did, maybe.

4

BONDI is flat country. The place is crowded with big blocks of flats, small ones, and divided houses in a pattern forced by the passionate desire of Australians to live by the sea as if they are reluctant to desert the fount of life. By day the suburb is a mixture of the smart and shabby; most of the buildings are painted white, but on some of them this gives way to green or grey at the sides. Some of the backs are grimy. Some of the gardens are smart and well watered; some feature palm trees tattered like old umbrellas in front of windows with faded, stained blinds.

Night changes all that. The neon glow compensates for the immense dark blankness of the sea. The haphazard levels of the buildings take on a foreign, exotic look and the penthouse dwellers sip their drinks high above the streets like fat, privileged eagles in their eyries.

I parked near the Regal again and strolled around the streets. There were too many cars for the air to be really pleasant, but the light breeze and the sea were doing their best. Up there in an eyrie with a scotch and a cigar, it would be pretty good. Food wouldn't be a problem; along the Parade you could eat Russian, Lebanese, Italian, Chinese and Indonesian and have a choice of places to do it in. You could take most of those culinary delights away, too, as well as the standard varieties of chicken and burger.

This profusion of food blunted my appetite. I walked, reflecting that these Bondi people were a breed apart; they ate out and lived on top of each other. Next to food joints, secondhand furniture places seemed to be the most common businesses. Those flats needed furniture, and I wondered if it was cheaper tenth hand than third hand. I doubted it.

The pubs were doing good business. So were the coffee bars, and a disco joint had the air of a car with its motor idling, waiting for the action to start. There were plenty of Asians and a few big, broad-featured Maoris among the street people. Humanity flowed freely along the main street, trickled down across the grass to the pavilion and sand and clustered in humming, twittering groups outside places of entertainment. The background to it all was the steady, pounding rhythm of money being spent.

I had one good contact in Bondi. Aldo Tomasetti is the brother of Primo, who runs a tattoo parlour in the Cross and who lets out a space at the back for me to park my car. Aldo is in the same game.

I tramped up Bondi Road two blocks back from the Parade and turned north. Aldo's place is a hole in the wall between a delicatessen and a place where women cater to the needs of men, credit cards accepted. The delicatessen was open and my appetite returned. I bought a sandwich and some orange juice and went into Aldo's.

He was working on an arm, a big, wide, fair-skinned arm that already had some snakes and dragons on it. Aldo was adding an eagle. The arm's owner grinned at me; he had a blank, comic-strip face and you could see why he wanted his body covered with pictures.

'Hey, Cliff,' Aldo said. 'Good to see you.'

'Excuse me eating,' I said.

'Have some wine with it. Flagon's over there.'

I got some paper cups and filled three with the red.

'You shouldn't drink for twenty-four hours after being tattooed,' Aldo said.

The customer looked alarmed and Aldo slapped his shoulder. 'I'm joking. Drink up. How's it going, Cliff?'

'Okay. Do you remember a guy named Singer? Used to own this and that around here?'

'Sure. Dead.'

'So they say.' I watched the tattooee carefully to see if there was any reaction to the name, but his face stayed blank. He

16

seemed to be enjoying the wine, though. I finished the sandwich and wiped my mouth with the wrapping paper.

'Did you ever hear anything different, Aldo? You know—boat offshore, frogmen, that sort of crap?'

'No, nothing like that. Was he kinky?'

'Not that I know. Why?'

'Just thinking. That Commander Crabb slept in his frog suit. Did you know that?'

'No.' I was aware of how little I knew about Singer. I didn't know how he talked, how he walked, what he drank. All essentials. I quizzed Aldo and he gave me the names of two hotels where Singer used to drink. One was on my list as one of his business interests. He also named three taxi drivers whose cabs Singer owned and he knew there were a good few more. There were no taxi drivers on my list.

To my great surprise, the customer spoke up brightly. 'You oughter look for Leon, mister. He knows everything that happens around here.'

'Thanks,' I said. 'Who's he?'

'Derro,' Aldo said. 'Wanders up and down. Funny guy. I once heard him speaking perfect Italian and you'd think he couldn't talk at all. Pissed all the time.'

I finished my wine and put the juice on the floor.

'Thanks again. Have some juice.'

'I'll give it to the girls next door for their vodka.'

I nodded and took a closer look at the tattoo. The tips of the eagle's wings were being inked in with brilliant reds and blues. My grandfather had had naval tattoos acquired in Port Said when he was fourteen; he used to show them to me fifty years later. One carried the name of his ship and he was still proud of it. I wondered whether John Singer had any tattoos.

So I hit the street with my photo and my list and my expense account. Although the pubs were busy, they hadn't reached that frenetic stage when everybody seems to be shouting while a full-scale brass band plays in the background. I had a discreet word to a barman here and a barmaid there, but drew blanks. I limited myself to half scotches with soda and ice, which made me belch but otherwise did little harm.

Mrs Singer was right; I did have something against pinball. The Punk Palace of Fun was a garish barn with strobe lights and brain-scrambling music. The machines gave out bleeps and blasts that the players seemed to understand and respond to. The non-players stared vacantly around them through their cigarette smoke; the users worked with the intensity of brain surgeons. The light sharpened their features, accentuated their youth. I felt the same kinship with them as I would with Chinese border guards.

At the back, in the shadows but not out of range of the noise, was a tiny recess with a table, a telephone and mine host. He was about thirty with sparse hair, a sunken chest and a grey, twitching face. He took a long look at the photo, which he held in a hand that vibrated like a musical saw.

'Could be. I dunno.'

'He's the owner. How long have you been here?'

'I dunno. Coupla years.'

'Have you ever seen this man?'

'I wouldn't see the owner, man. I manage for a guy who rents. *He* might rent from someone else, for all I know.'

'You might have seen him somewhere else. On the street?'

'Could be.'

I got ten dollars out and put it on the table, keeping my index finger down hard on one corner of the note.

'Think.'

'I could ask around.'

I got out one of my cards, put it on top of the note and took my finger off. He grabbed with one of his dancing hands. He'd spend the money on something to put in a vein or up his nose and wouldn't remember who had given him the card or why, but you never knew.

'Give me a call if anything comes.'

He nodded jerkily. I went out onto the street and turned towards the last Bondi place on the list, a snooker room. I was thinking that it wasn't a promising start when a kid stepped out of a doorway and asked me for a light.

'I don't . . .' He hit me low and hard and I gasped, feeling the fluid rise inside me. Then my arm was grabbed and swung and I had to go with it or break it. I went, spinning out of control off the street into a lane, where my back hit a wall with an impact that shook my teeth. They came at me, two of them, with a third hanging back. I was shaky and just managed to get a knee up into one of them before the other threw a punch that got me on the neck.

I sagged and would have been a sitting duck for the next punch, but it never came. Someone moved behind my play-mates and hooked the legs of one neatly out from under him. He didn't even watch the effect of that; the other kid swung around and my saviour hit him just above the belt. There were three sounds: a *whuump* as the punch landed, a grunt from the guy who delivered it and a scream from the recipient. The third guy, the non-participant, ran down the lane and the one who went down first scrambled up and ran after him. The unluckiest of the trio lay on the ground, fighting for breath.

I straightened up. My deliverer gripped my arm and I felt the immense strength in his hold.

'Easy,' he said.

'I'm okay, thanks. That was a great punch.'

He looked down at the figure on the ground; he was young and slight.

'He was overmatched,' he said. 'I was the light heavyweight champion of Oregon, amateur.'

'I believe you.' I peered down at the kid. I'd never seen him before; he was pimply and smelt a bit.

The light heavyweight champion of Oregon let go of my arm and gave me his hand to shake. I took it carefully.

'Bruce Henneberry.'

'Cliff Hardy. Henneberry? Really?'

'Sure. Why?'

'He was a fighter here, good one. Fred Henneberry.'

'That right? Now, what was this here?'

'I don't know.' The kid was crawling now, back towards the street, and Henneberry put a leg across his path.

'You show any money out on the street?'

'Yes, a bit.'

'Junkies most likely, then.' He bent down for a closer look at the kid. 'Scabs, skin and bone. Hopped up—junkie for sure. After your cash.'

'Let him go,' I said wearily. 'He'll be bruised for weeks.' He lifted his leg and the kid got up and walked off shakily as if his legs were made of tin.

During the action, Henneberry had looked to be of middle height or under, but now I could see that he was nearly as tall as me. He'd been in a fighter's crouch, for one thing, and for another he was so solidly built that he didn't look tall. His shoulders were huge and he had the sort of neck and chest that are built up by weight training. He wouldn't have made the light heavyweight limit now. His face was wide and open and his brown hair was cut short.

'I need a drink,' I said.

'How about brandy and coffee? I know a place.'

'Fine. How far?'

'Close. Let's go.'

We walked; he was not quite supporting me, but ready to do so. I tried to think of what I knew about Oregon and couldn't come up with much—capital Portland, industries, timber and fish. Not sparkling openers.

'Ah, Cliff, do you mind me asking what you were doing flashing your roll on Hill Street?'

'I wasn't exactly flashing it. I'm looking for someone. I was buying information.'

He stopped in mid-stride. 'You're not a cop?'

'Private enquiries. Why?'

'I don't want to screw up. Helping a cop wouldn't help me.'

We got moving again and he steered me into a small court that was flanked by boutiques, a cake shop and a surf shop. It struck me that Bondi was light on for outdoorsy places like surf shops. There was a dark window at the end of the court, dimly lit from inside, with an illuminated sign saying 'Manny's' over the door.

'This is my base,' Henneberry said. 'Manny keeps a bottle under the coffee machine.'

5

YOU couldn't have read the *Times* inside Manny's, but it wasn't like the interior of a coal bin either. There were a few people sitting around smoking and drinking coffee and a few were even talking. It was an intellectual sort of place. We sat down and a short, dark character with long, oiled hair bustled over. He wore a Charlie Chan moustache and looked like a walking mixture of the Orient, the Middle East and the decadent West. His white safari suit was spotless and he sported some gold jewellery around his solid neck and on his capable-looking hands.

'Manfred,' Henneberry said. 'Meet Cliff Hardy.'

I shook my second power-packed hand for the evening. Manny kept his strength in check so that his grip was almost flaccid, but the force was there.

'What'll you have, Bruce?'

'Coffee with,' Henneberry said. 'Cliff just had a dust-up with some junkies on Hill Street.'

'He did the fighting,' I said.

Manny nodded. 'I hope you didn't break any bones, Bruce.' From the way he said it, I had the feeling that Manny might have broken a few in his time.

'Nah,' Henneberry said. 'I just raised my voice some.'

Manny grinned and looked as though he'd like to hear more, but he remembered his role and moved smoothly over towards the coffee machine.

'Base for what?' I said.

'Excuse me?'

'You said this was your base and I was wondering about your operation.'

He laughed, showing his expensively cared-for American teeth and the imposing circumference of that built-up neck. I reckoned it at seventeen inches of bone and muscle you could break a hand on.

'Well, I'm a journalist. Freelance, you know? I've got a commission to do a series on the drug problem here on the beach. That's why I was hoping you weren't a cop. Now it'll get around that I saved some dude from getting mugged tonight. That's not very cool, but it'd be worse if you were a cop. Who're you looking for, Cliff? Maybe I can help. I've been working here a couple of weeks now.'

The coffee came, which gave me time to think about an answer. Bruce seemed extraordinarily physical for a journalist. Most of those I knew could scarcely get the glass to their mouths without help, but Americans are a different race.

I stalled. 'Who're you working for, Bruce?'

'Oh, *National News*, right here.'

That would be so easy to check that it looked as if he was telling the truth. Also he had a way with him, a frankness and openness that might have been professional but didn't come across that way. I sipped some of the brandy-laced coffee with appreciation.

'I'm looking into the alleged disappearance of a guy named John Singer. Seems he went into the water around two years ago and hasn't come out yet.'

He drank some coffee. 'Good guy or bad guy?'

'Bit of both. There's a whisper that he's still with us. I'm checking it out.'

'I never heard of him; sorry. But I could ask on the street.'

'What are you doing, exactly?'

'Oh, I . . . ah . . . hang around and talk to the kids. Truth is, I feel more like a social worker than a writer. I've helped a few of the kids get out of the shit and go home. Not many.'

'Plenty left?'

'Sure.'

We drained our cups and he raised two fingers to Manny, who obliged quickly. The brandy did me a power of good; I had only a dull ache where the kid had hit. My pride hurt, but a few drinks is good for that, too.

'Do the drugs get sold in the pinball parlours?'

'Yeah, and in the pubs, in cars, on the beach. You name it.'

'How's it organised?'

'Now, that's a big question.' He took a cassette out of his jeans pocket and tapped it on the table. 'I'm going to rap to this a little. You can listen in if you want.'

He went across the room, reached under a bench and pulled up a cassette recorder. Back at the table he took a gulp of coffee, put the cassette into the machine and got out a small notebook, which he consulted while he talked softly into the microphone. He was naming names and sums of money and recalling direct speech. He spoke for about fifteen minutes before clicking the recorder off.

'Here's the thing,' he said. 'I'm sort of in harness with this sociologist named Ann Winter. She's working the same route as me, but for her PhD. She's living right in the middle of the shit. We leave these cassettes for each other. Sort of swap information, you know? She goes more on the female angle. I tell you, it's mean.'

I expressed a polite interest, but not much more. My business brings me into contact with a lot of people who do not share in this world's joys—old whores of one sort or another, washed-up fighters, gaolbirds and drunks. I never heard of a city from Pompeii onwards that didn't have them in good measure, and they'll still be with us when disco and skateboards are history. You have to take the long view.

I was thinking that, as so often happened, I was off to a bad start. I'd hardly made a dent in the enquiry if all I'd achieved was to leave a freelance journo on the trail while I went off to bed with an ache in the midsection. Then Henneberry sat up straight and pulled in his slight stomach bulge.

'Here's Ann,' he said.

Even in the half light, even in her dirty jeans and nondescript shirt, she was something special. She was tall, close to six feet in her medium-heeled boots. She had a bandanna around her wild, straggly black hair, and with her dark eyes and the big denim bag she carried she looked like a gypsy. *Winter*, I thought, *a good outdoors country name. Maybe she is a gypsy.* She thumped down heavily into the chair next to Henneberry and flopped a tobacco pouch and matches up onto the table.

'I'm buggered,' she said.

I tried to keep my eyes uninterested and my jaw firm, but Henneberry was beyond help. 'Hey, hey, Annie,' he stammered, 'you'll want a drink. Manny!'

'Just the coffee, Bruce,' she said. 'If he puts that bloody grappa in it, I'll fall asleep right here.' She made a cigarette the right way, keeping more tobacco at the ends than in the middle and evening it up in the rolling. She stuck it in her mouth, lit it and inhaled and threw her head back to expel the smoke. She had a nice neck with dark, straggling hairs growing low on it.

She noticed me noticing. 'Ann Winter,' she said. 'Hello.'

Bruce turned back from trying to catch Manny's attention. 'This is Cliff Hardy, Annie.'

I nodded and she pushed the tobacco at me. I pushed it back.

'I thought you might want it, from the way you were watching.'

'No,' I said. 'I used to roll them. Gave it up. I just liked the way you did it. Good.'

She blew smoke over my head. 'For a woman, you mean. Shit, there's girls around here who can roll them one-handed in the dark.'

'What do they do with the other hand?'

'Almost anything.' She laughed, the coffee arrived and she shovelled sugar into it. Henneberry watched her like a gambler watching the deal.

'I need it,' she said. 'Must've walked fifteen miles today.'

'How come?' I asked.

She glanced at Henneberry, who gave her a lightning sketch of the encounter in the alley, as he called it. He made us sound like allies in a great and noble cause. She nodded and looked at me directly as she spoke.

'One of the girls is going cold turkey and she's on a weight-losing kick with it. She weighs twenty stone, near enough, and she's walking it off. She said she'd tell me all about how she got that way. She's serious. We went ten miles, I reckon.'

'How did she get so fat?' Henneberry said. 'What's that, three hundred pounds?'

'Nearly,' Ann said. 'You wouldn't believe it. She worked in a place that specialised in fat girls. The manager force fed them. She just blew up. Want to hear it?' She got a cassette out of the bag. Bruce took it and put his hand on her shoulder. She didn't shake it off, but she didn't nuzzle into it with her cheek either. I showed her the picture of Singer and she looked at it carefully, slanting it to get more light.

'Don't know him,' she said. 'Wouldn't mind, though.'

Henneberry glanced sharply at her and I could sense the short circuits and sparks in their connection. I was surprised to find myself pleased by it. Henneberry kept talking, but she was bored by him; she smoked and her dark eyes drifted around the room registering and recording. They came to rest on me.

'I never heard that Singer was connected with drugs and girls,' I said. 'But you never know with the smart ones. I'd be glad if you'd ask around, Ann.'

She nodded. 'There's a guy named McLeary who runs a lot of the massage places closer to the city. Most of the girls I know are streeties, but they drift in and out of the houses. One of the older ones might know something about your bloke, but you never know.' She gave me another one of her direct looks. 'He might have fancied the younger ones.'

'It's a wicked world,' I said.

I thanked Henneberry and told him he threw a good punch, just like Fred. He'd forgotten my earlier remark and looked puzzled, then camouflaged his puzzlement in talk.

'Say, Cliff, why don't you check back with me? I might turn up something on your man.' He dug into Ann's bag for a pen and scribbled on a paper napkin. 'Give me a call.'

I got out some money, but he waved it away. 'Next time,' he said.

I gave him a card instead, and passed one across to Ann. She fiddled with the tobacco and I took the pouch and made a cigarette, about the hundred and fifty thousandth I'd made. She opened her lips and let me put it in.

'Thanks,' she said.

I looked back as I left the place. Henneberry had his face close to Ann's and he was talking again. Manny loomed up massively behind them with a hand outstretched for Bruce's cup. He saw me looking at him and winked like an Irishman. It looked obscene on that sallow, culturally complex face. I walked back to my car, thinking about gypsies, Levantines and Americans. Then I wondered what nationality the twenty-stone whore was.

6

I HAD some aspirin and a touch more brandy for the stomach when I got home so I slept late. Hilde had gone when I got up. The *News* was neatly folded on the kitchen table and there was a manilla envelope on top of it. I opened the flap and slid out the photograph. John Singer looked up at me through crinkled, squinting eyes; he had several days' growth of beard and his hair was fluffed out untidily. He looked much less like Caine than he had in the other picture.

The photograph seemed to reproach me. Singer had a challenging, macho look: I could interpret it as catch-me-if-you-can or would-you-have-the-guts-to-do-what-I've-done or, instead, I could stare right back at him and think he wasn't so tough after all. It was a funny case. I could spend a few days on the streets getting negative responses, and that could be construed as a positive result. It wasn't the way I liked to work.

I shaved, showered, and made and ate a breakfast that was also lunch. The *News* contained no news; at home we had problems between the states and the Federal government, not over principles but over money. Overseas, oil was going up and gold was going down; what that meant was anybody's guess. The people who had the oil probably had all the gold they wanted, anyway.

After eating, I felt more resourceful. I had Bruce Henneberry to follow up on, I could contact Singer's doctor to find out if he could have had anything nasty on his mind and there was always the Punk Palace of Fun. The creepy manager and my friends in the laneway could have been connected and could relate to my enquiries.

I opened the previous day's mail, but it was just as boring as it had looked the day before. Mrs Singer's envelope had been hand delivered. I phoned her.

'Did you get the picture?' she asked. 'I had someone run it over.'

Who said it's hard to get help these days? 'Yeah, I got it. Thanks. Can you give me the name of your husband's doctor, please?'

'Whatever for?'

'People tell doctors things they don't tell wives. Have you seen much of him lately?'

'No, I'm never ill. I'm sure . . .'

'Sure of what?'

'I was going to say I'm sure the police would have checked on that, but now I come to think of it the police hardly checked on anything.'

'They're busy,' I said. 'The name, please.'

She gave it to me—a Dr Burgess in a clinic at Randwick that sounded like money.

'Any progress?'

'Not yet. Did anyone ever tell your husband that he looked like Michael Caine?'

'Yes, often. Why?'

'It makes it harder. Not as hard as if he looked like Robert Redford, but people get confused.'

'Do you need more money?' she asked quickly.

I was surprised. Offering more money is a serious step, the most serious step. She seemed to sense from my silence that she'd made a wrong move, and she covered up quickly. 'I thought you might need extra people or something.'

'No,' I said. 'I'll manage. Thanks, Mrs Singer. I'll be in touch.'

I got out the wine and ice and soda and made myself the first drink of the day while I thought things over. I had my second drink and thought some more. It felt wrong; the hand delivered envelope, the offer of money. I felt pushed and I didn't like it.

I felt the tobacco craving creeping up on me, as it always did when I tried to think my way around corners. It was lucky I didn't play chess because I'd have cracked. But I told myself it was the wine, the long-associated habits of drinking and smoking, and I had some more wine.

I rang Dr Burgess at the Money Inc Clinic and was told that he'd gone on holiday for a fortnight. That was nice; there's nothing like a holiday to tone a doctor up. I then rang the number Henneberry had given me, but it didn't answer. That left only the Punk Palace, and it was a good few hours too early for that. I killed the time the way a civilised man should; I did some exercises very carefully on account of my bruised stomach and read several chapters of *The World According to Garp*. The thought of my tennis shoes getting dusty in the cupboard reproved me and I resolved to get back to it when the Singer case was over.

I was still reading when the phone rang.

'Cliff Hardy? This is Ann Winter.'

'Yes?' I didn't mean to sound abrupt, but something in her voice told me that she hadn't rung me up to invite me around for a drink.

'Look, I'm worried about Bruce. He was supposed to meet me here and he hasn't showed up. He should be here. I've rung his flat, but there's no answer. I thought you might know where he is.'

'No, Ann, I don't. I rang his flat, too.'

'He left a cassette and he sounds really weird on it. There's some stuff about you.'

'What sort of stuff?'

'Well, some names and places. Manny says he rushed off after he left the cassette. This is touchy stuff we're into here and we're very careful. We leave these messages . . .'

'I know; Bruce told me a bit about it. You stay at Manny's. Tell me where Bruce lives and I'll go there. Give me the number of Manny's place and I'll call you if I find anything.'

She gave me the information. I tossed down the rest of my drink and went out to the car.

Bronte is a notch or two further down the socio-economic scale than Bondi. The flats are smaller and less flash and there are weatherboard cottages that look as though they haven't changed since the 1920s. I drove pretty fast, partly out of pleas-

30

ure that the car would move like that, partly out of an instinct that there was some kind of trouble brewing. The streets got narrow towards Bronte and I had to be careful to avoid joggers and a few unhappy-looking guys working on old cars jacked up in front of blocks of flats.

Bruce's flat was in a white, waterfall-style building up over the rise, well back from Bronte beach. The waterfall effect was achieved by two cylindrical towers that flanked a flat-roofed central section. If it had been up to me I'd have taken my rooms in the right-hand tower on the top floor—best view. It turned out that Bruce's place was in the left hand tower. His door was at the back, away from the street and at the top of a set of exterior stairs like a fire escape. The backyard was concreted over and only six rotary clothes lines grew there.

I knocked on the door and was answered by silence. I beat heavily on it and got more silence. The stairs were placed centrally, too far away to get a look through the window.

I stood there, wondering why I knew something was wrong, why I knew I wasn't just standing outside the door of someone who wasn't home. Then I got it; there was a smell coming from around the edges of the door. I squatted and sniffed. There was a stench of shit.

The Falcon may present a more respectable front these days, but fundamentally it's the same old car. I got my .45 automatic from under the dashboard and a short jemmy from the boot. I splintered the door jamb and smashed the lock, then I kicked the door open and waited, flattened back against the wall. Nothing moved. Nothing happened, except that the smell grew stronger.

Bruce Henneberry lay on his back, about three feet from the door. He made one of the worst corpses I'd ever seen, including those the guerrillas had played about with before and after death in Malaya, and I had to lean against the broken door and mutter things and get a grip on myself. I looked out into the yard and beyond, but my break-and-enter had disturbed no-one.

I used the jemmy to ease the door shut and stepped into the room. There had been a hell of a lot of blood in Henneberry, and the carpet was thick and sticky with it. I skirted that and the body and looked around the flat, still trying to get control and make normal observations.

The flat was in character; there were a lot of books of the kind that people who love to talk, love to read—Joan Didion, Toffler, Galbraith. They were in the standard student bookcase; bricks and plain pine planking. That and a couple of chairs and a TV set with a telephone on top of it comprised the furniture of the room in which Henneberry had died. His bedroom was spartan; double mattress on the floor with tangled bedclothes, more books, some clothes thrown over a Chinese saucer chair and some put away roughly in a chest of drawers. There were marijuana cigarette butts in a saucer by the bed. The bathroom was a bit streaky but basically clean; the kitchen was neat and didn't look as if much food preparation went on there. A cassette player was plugged into a wall point; Henneberry evidently did his writing on the kitchen table. The light was good there and I found filing cards, manilla folders with notes, news clippings and other stuff in a cardboard box under the table. There were also a portable typewriter, a small plastic bag containing marijuana and cigarette papers and a half-empty bottle of brandy.

All journalists keep an address book. Some combine this with a sort of diary, but there was no sign of any such item. That left the body and the nasty part. I squatted down just beyond the bloody swamp and tried to suspend all senses while I felt around Bruce. He'd been wearing jeans and an army shirt with deep front pockets and I found his wallet in one of them. I finger-tipped through it, but it was functional, nothing more. There was no diary, no address book. I got blood on my hands and went into the bathroom to wash it off. I'd been right about the bathroom the first time—there was no message written in soap on the mirror and nothing written in blood on the walls.

I looked at my face in the mirror. I'd been sweating and my hair flopped down lankly onto my forehead. I was blinking convulsively and the search had given me a fixed, long-faced look, like a wax dummy. If someone had walked in, put a knife in my hand and said, 'He did it', I'd have believed it.

I went out and looked at Henneberry again. His face was black, half of his intestines lay on the carpet beside him and he smelled like an open drain. I used the phone.

'Manny's.'

'Ann Winter, please.' Pause.

'Ann Winter.'

'Hardy. Get Manny to pour you a brandy.'

'I don't want brandy, I . . .'

'Do it!'

'Okay, I've got it. Now what?'

'Bruce is dead. He's been murdered. Drink the brandy.'

There was a pause and her voice came through again harshly.

'All right. I'm all right. Are you sure . . . it's . . . not an accident or anything?'

'No accident. Look, I'm going to have to phone the cops now, and they'll look you up pretty soon. I don't know whether this is connected with what you're doing or with what I'm doing. Any ideas on that?'

'No. I told you we were careful. I don't think we've trodden on any big toes, but I don't know . . .'

'Okay. Did Bruce have an address book, diary, notebook, anything like that?'

'Yes.'

'It's not here. That must mean something, but I don't know what. Have you got that cassette?'

'Yes.'

'Hang on to it. Don't give it to the cops. Who else knows about it?'

'Well, Manny.'

'Will he keep quiet?'

'I think so. He's . . .'

'Okay, I know he's there. You'd better go home. I'll have to give your name to the police. Will the university have an address for you?'

'No, only my supervisor, Dr Kenneth Badly.'

'Right, I'll give them that. It'll take them a while to get to

33

you and give you time to think. I take it you don't mind holding
out on the police a bit?'

'Are you kidding? After what I've heard? No. But I want to
see . . .'

'No, you don't. Believe me, you don't. Give me your home
number and I'll talk to you later.'

She did, and I rang off. Talking and acting in the real world
of the living had steadied me, and I was able to take a closer
look at Bruce. The killer had put something thin and strong
around his neck and pulled. It would probably have been impossible to strangle someone of Bruce's build with bare hands, but
even with the garotte it hadn't been easy; marks on the neck
suggested that Bruce had got a hand up under the cord or had
got leverage somehow. That had brought the knife into play. It
looked as if the killer had cut and had gone on strangling.

I took a last look around the flat to see if there was anything
more to be learned. There wasn't, but I found something I'd
missed before. Down by the bed was a small bronze statuette
mounted on a wooden block. A plate on the block read: 'BRUCE
HENNEBERRY' and below 'CHAMPION LIGHT HEAVYWEIGHT
DIVISION, A.A.L.O. 1977'. It hadn't done him much good.

I called the cops. While I was waiting for them, I called my
lawyer Cy Sackville and put him in the picture.

'Are you sure you didn't do it?' he asked.

'He was the light heavyweight champion of Oregon and I
haven't used a disembowelling knife in years.'

'Well, just play a straight bat with the police. Stonewall, you
know.'

'Trevor Bailey,' I agreed.

'What?'

'Nothing. I just wanted to see if you knew what you were
talking about. How about my client? D'you think I can keep
her out of it?'

'Depends how hard they squeeze your balls. If I don't hear
from you in, say, six hours, I'll start making noises. Okay?'

7

I SAT in a chair with my jemmy in my lap and waited. Two uniformed men came in; they looked at the body and looked at me and didn't know what to say. Then Detective Sergeant Frank Parker arrived, and he knew just what to say. He issued orders in a rapid stream that set the patrol boys running and summoned technicians who photographed, dusted and measured in the way they do. He wandered around the flat after telling me to stay where I was. He was very tall and well-groomed with an expensive suit and good manners. I stayed put and watched him being efficient; it really was too soon to tell whether or not he had any brains.

He certainly scored on style. His directives to the technical people suggested that he knew what they were doing and that they knew he knew. He bent down to look at things and didn't seem to be worried about the crease in his nice dark blue pants; more points scored. When all the activity was going to his satisfaction, he called me out to the kitchen. I handed him the jemmy.

'Illegal tool,' he said. He had a good voice, like the voices you hear on the taxi radios but a bit smoother.

I shrugged. That's when he told me his name and offered me a filter cigarette. I refused the smoke and he asked to see my papers, quite politely. He looked through them quickly and handed them back. He seemed to be about to snap his fingers as a way of asking to see the .45, but he stopped himself. I passed the gun across and he gave it a quick once over. He put it on the table and we both looked at it.

'The licence isn't for that gun,' he said. So he did have brains. 'Where's the .38?' he added quietly.

'At home.'

'This is your car gun?'

'Right.'

'Sit down, Hardy.' He reached across to drop his ash in the sink and stayed in a leaning position, very relaxed. He wasn't easily placed as a copper; not one of the old belt-'em-by-accident-before-you-do-it-on-purpose types who might or might not be honest and not one of the new, flashy types who are interested in your money and their careers and who play a balancing game by their rules.

He got out a notebook that had been spoiling the sit of his jacket pocket and wrote down my name and address from memory.

'What was the licence number again?'

I told him and he wrote some more. Then he said, 'Excuse me', and stuck his head out the door. He looked into the living-room for a minute and wrote some more before he put the notebook away.

'We'll need a full statement, of course. What do you want to tell me now?' He stubbed out the cigarette in the sink and with it went the slight informality. He was all business now.

'Not much to tell,' I said. 'I only met him yesterday.'

'Maybe that was his unlucky day.'

'Maybe, but I can't see how.'

'Let's start with how you met him.'

It dawned on me that this was all technique with him. Leaning there in his sharp but uncared-for suit, with his hair a bit long and his voice almost professionally persuasive, he was like a cat with claws in. If you weren't careful, you'd be telling him how much you fiddled on your income tax and all about the shoplifting you'd done back in the 1950s. I dug in a bit.

'You've seen my papers, Parker. You know what I do for a living. I think a formal statement might be the best move and you can make up your mind what to do after that.'

He didn't like it, and straightened up a little towards the six foot three which would give him two inches on me. Before he could speak, there was some swearing from the living-room. From the curses I gathered that the men were trying to prepare the body so they could move it. It wouldn't have been a nice job and you couldn't blame them for swearing. Parker took a look out—I didn't—and when he turned back to me his face was a bit less hawkish and hard-lined.

I looked down at the Colt on the table and wondered if my ex-wife Cyn hadn't been right all along about this job. 'You deal with damaged people,' she'd told me, 'because you're damaged yourself. You can't operate with normal, decent people.' She claimed that I mauled her decent people unless I was drunk, when I'd make fun of them to their faces. She said that my policeman mate Grant Evans and I were violence-prone anti-socials. She said Evans and I belonged in gaol with the other social rejects. She said a lot of things as our marriage crumbled.

Parker pushed the gun towards me to show he was a good guy and said, 'College Street, now,' to show he was a hard guy. He let me follow him to town in my own car, but he noted down the registration number and he didn't give me back my jemmy.

We went into one of the bleak, soulless rooms at Police Head-quarters and I gave a statement to a stenographer that left out certain details such as Mrs Singer's name and the coffee bar meeting place. Parker looked in from time to time and listened to me talking. He didn't seem to like what he heard. When the statement was typed up, he brought it to me for signing.

The room was getting to me by then and I had a delayed reaction to the whole foul business. 'You don't look too good,' he said. 'We'll get some coffee and go up to the office.'

I could see why he didn't say 'my office'. Parker shared a room with three other detectives. They had the nasty view into east Sydney from their windows. Their desks were wedged in between filing cabinets and wastepaper baskets. A colleague at his desk kept his head down and ignored us.

I got a cup of coffee, was offered the comforts of tobacco again and sat at one of the detective's desks while Parker read the statement. He didn't seem to have any trouble with any of the longer words. He smoked his filter tip down far enough not to be a wastrel but not so far as to get all the packed-up gunk into his lungs. He finished reading.

'Client's name?' he asked.

I shook my head.

'Any marks where this kid hit you?'

I wasn't sure myself; I pulled up my shirt and there was a light bruise, hardly visible. I'd probably made a little too much of it in the statement.

'Bit slow, were you, Hardy?'

'I'd had a few drinks.'

'Have a few more with Henneberry?'

'Yes.'

'Where?'

I named one of the pubs I'd visited that night. What I'd said probably wouldn't hold up and the lie could turn Parker nasty, but it was the best I could do off the cuff. It was stuffy in the room and Parker took off his jacket and rolled up the sleeves. He had thin, sinewy forearms and the right one had a long white scar running along it. He saw me look at it.

'Knife,' he said. 'Nasty things, knives. I don't like to think of someone out there who can use one the way this bloke did. Do you?'

'No.'

'You might run into him, and Henneberry's not going to be around to protect you.' He got a nice bit of needle into that. 'There might be no-one around at all. Have you thought of that?'

'Yeah, but I don't know if Henneberry's death has anything to do with my little matter. I'm happy to go on with it for a while.'

'Go on doing what?' he asked sharply.

I grinned at him and shrugged. He leaned forward across the paper and files and other bureaucratic junk on his desk. 'I have to try and find this maniac, Hardy. You look like a nuisance to me. I can keep you out of the area if I want to.'

I knew he could do it, and it was time to decide how to play him. Since Grant Evans got stuck at a high-middle level in the Force and threw it in to take a Deputy Commissionership interstate, I hadn't an ally in the Police Department. It was a sad lack and maybe Parker could fill the role. I'd liked his style so far, particularly the way he hadn't threatened to throw me down any stairs.

'Do two things for me,' I said. 'Call Grant Evans in the west and ask him what he thinks of me. I think you'll be satisfied. If you are, give me two days clear on it. I'll give you anything I get. In two days I should find out what I want to know, anyway.'

'Whatever the fuck that is,' he growled. 'What do I put in the report in the meantime?'

I reached forward and poked a finger into the paper on the desk top. 'Reports,' I said. 'What's in these, d'you reckon? You can say what you like in a report. You can say I've been warned, if you like. I won't contradict you.'

He looked at the paper jungle in front of him with distaste. 'Okay, Hardy. I don't have to call Evans. We've got a note or two about you here and I looked at it while you were yapping. You're sneaky, you hit a lot of lobs, but your sheet's pretty clean. Lately, anyhow.'

'You play tennis, do you?'

'Yes. Pennant. You?'

'Yeah, not pennant, though. Do I get the two days?'

His look seemed to measure me, weigh me and estimate my IQ. 'You know,' he said slowly, 'I actually got some sleep last night. Good sleep. You're benefiting. Piss off, I've got a report to write.'

I called Sackville from a phone booth outside the police building and then I called Ann Winter. She coughed as soon as she answered.

'Sorry, I've been smoking non-stop. What's happening?'

'Not much. A pretty smart cop is on the job. Can I come over and hear the cassette?'

'I'm at the dump; there's no recorder here. Look, come over and get me. We can go to my people's place and play it. I don't want to stay here tonight, anyway.'

I drove back to Bondi and located the dump, which it was. The street was two-thirds taken over by apartment blocks and Ann's place was a set of semi-detached, two-storey houses that looked as if their owners had decided to sell later when the price was right. The houses were blighted; guttering drooped, slates were missing on the roofs and a couple of the windows were blanked out by sheets of tin nailed up behind shattered glass. The brick fence had collapsed and the concrete path to the door of the house on the right was cracked and lumpy. It was a good bet that the other paths would be the same. The whole lot was waiting to be levelled so that ten storeys of glass and pre-poured concrete could rise on the site.

I knocked on the ramshackle door and Ann came down some creaking stairs to open it. A smell of fried food and damp wafted over me.

'Choice, isn't it?' she said. 'Come on, let's go.'

She gave me an address in Point Piper and I drove there, trying to hold myself together against the culture shock. We pulled up in front of a high wall that looked as if it was shielding half a million dollars worth of house. It was like taking Cinderella away from the housework and up to the palace.

8

ANN Winter's daddy's house was the sort of place you could
visit late at night without waking anyone up. It was built
in wings around a swimming pool and a couple of courtyard
gardens. I upped the price to three-quarters of a million as we
moved through it. We went in by some floor-to-ceiling glass
doors and down a carpeted corridor to a bedroom. From the
familiar way she threw her cardigan onto the bed and kicked
her shoes off against the wall, I took this to be Ann's room. It
had just about everything you'd want: books, a big TV set, a
double bed, an exercise bike, a turntable, big speakers and a
cassette player.

'D'you want a drink?' She waved a hand at a cupboard under
the bookcase.

'No, I want to hear the cassette.'

She took it out of her bag and slipped it into the machine.
'I'm going to wash.' She punched the 'play' button and went
out of the room. Bruce Henneberry's drawling voice blocked out
the sound of water running.

'October 3,' he said, 'One pm. Two items for Cliff Hardy. One,
Leon. Talked to him this morning. He knows things and he'll
talk for money. I got an interesting sample—social security scam.
Two, the Mellow Yellows. Ashram on Salisbury Street. Guy I
saw is Brother Gentle. Off the planet but knows the oldies. Have
notes. Have to run, will fill in later.'

I played it through again. Ann came back into the room with
a freshened-up look. She leaned against the wall and listened.

'Pretty cryptic,' I said. 'Was it always like that?'

'No, that's just a notes tape. It's not cryptic. Leon, he's a wino
who lives near Bruce. He's the real thing—picks up cigarette
butts in the street, pisses in public. He's been charged with

exposing himself hundreds of times, does a few days or weeks and they let him out. He's around, no-one notices him, he probably hears things.'

'Mellow Yellows?'

'Meditation freaks. Salisbury Street, as Bruce says. Said.' She stopped and looked at me. I was sitting on the bed and I wondered if she was recalling being in it with Henneberry.

'Shit,' she said. 'Shit, shit, shit. You still haven't told me how Bruce died. Was he shot, or what?'

'He was stabbed,' I said.

'It would be something sneaky like that. He was so brave, you know?'

'I know. I saw him in action.'

She gave a sour laugh. 'He came over here to avoid the draft initially. Then he went back and came out again. He was so nice. Some of the kids . . .' She broke off and went over to the cupboard, which turned out to be a small refrigerator-cum-bar. she got out a can of beer and held it up. I nodded and she got another one. We popped our cans and I suppose we drank a toast to the late champ.

'You make him sound like a crusader,' I said. 'Crusaders in that business get stomped on.'

She shook her head hard. 'He wasn't crusading.'

The image of Henneberry on his living-room floor was still sharp in my mind and I didn't want to talk about him in case I let it slip that 'stabbed' wasn't exactly right. I pointed to the cassette player.

'Who would have heard this besides you?'

She drank some more beer, showing me that nice neck again.

'Hell, I don't know. People at Manny's could have heard it. They play music tapes on the same machine. Our stuff gets mixed up with it sometimes.'

'Doesn't sound very secure.'

'That's what I thought, but Bruce said it was. You hide shit in the barnyard, he said.'

Yanks, I thought. 'Did you leave tapes every day?'

'No, not every day. But he was going to turn up with one

today for sure.' She finished her beer and set the can down on the floor. Then she dropped down beside it and let her long legs sprawl out on the thick, white carpet. She bit her lip. 'Sometimes he'd just sing the "Star Spangled Banner" or quote a poem ...'

I nodded. 'Did he ever make copies of a tape?'

'Yes, if it was something important. One for him and one for me.'

I thought back to the layout in the flat. No cassettes around. 'Would it upset you too much to play it again?' I asked.

She scrambled across to the fridge. 'I'm going to get pissed tonight. Let's hear it again.' She got a half bottle of Southern Comfort from the bar and a nice Swedish-looking glass. She asked me if I wanted a drink, I said, 'No', and she rewound the tape and played it again. She poured out a big dollop of the booze and knocked it back while I listened closely, trying to pick up background noise. There was traffic, conversation and the sound of things being put down.

'Manny's?' I said.

'Could be.'

I reached over to recover the tape, but the machine was too complicated for me. She pressed the right button and I lifted the cassette out. I was very conscious of her, close and smelling of tobacco and Southern Comfort. She had a patterned cardigan on over a skivvy; her jeans were white but dirty and her feet were bare. She looked more like a gypsy than ever with her hair tangling down onto her shoulders.

'Do you like this room?' she asked suddenly.

I glanced around critically. 'I'm too poor to like it,' I said.

She emptied her glass and topped it up. 'Bruce didn't like it, and he was rich.'

I could feel the cracks opening in her tough facade and the development of a jumpy, unpredictable logic that might help her through her pain but that only she could follow. I'd seen it before.

'Well, there's a lot here ...'

'Here!' She waved her free hand at the walls that had posters on them that looked hand-painted and the shelf of hard-cover books. 'There's nothing here, nothing! You should see the rest of the place. Wanna see it?'

When it came to prostitution and drugs she was as tough as she needed to be, but death was another matter. Maybe she'd never had any direct contact with it before, coming from that Point Piper cocoon. An instinct told me that no comfort from me would be welcome.

'Another time. I've got to go. Will you be all right?'

'D'you mean will I take pills or something?' She gave a skittish laugh and raised her glass. 'Not me. I'll bomb out on this. I'll be back in Bondi tomorrow.'

'Why don't you give yourself a few days off?'

'It's worse here than there, believe me. Come on, I'll show you back out to the real world.'

We went back the way we'd come, noiselessly.

'The police'll be onto you soon. I was a bit vague about you when I talked to them. I'd be grateful if you could be a bit vague about me.'

'No worries,' she said. 'I'll be feminine, it's the only way with cops.'

I drove off wondering how feminine wiles would work on Frank Parker. Then I wondered how masculine wiles would work on Ann Winter.

Hilde was still up and watching television when I got home.

'That killing in Bondi,' she said. 'I saw it on the news. Nothing to do with you, was it?'

'You didn't really see it. Yeah, it was everything to do with me. I found him.'

'Ugh. How was it?'

I was tired and frustrated, full of confused half-thoughts with no connections. Like most people, I take those moods out on someone else and Hilde was the nearest to hand. 'How do you think it was?' I snapped. 'It was fucking messy. You work in a pink and white world don't you, Hilde, love?'

She tried to weather the storm with a light touch. 'There's some yellow in it.'

44

'Well, intestines, *guts*, are grey and green. Did you know that?'

She didn't say anything, just looked blankly at the shimmering screen. She'd turned the sound down and people with orange faces and blue hair were whispering to each other. Within seconds I was sorry for what I'd said. I told her so.

'It's all right,' she said. 'You get like that. It's stress.'

'Why don't you move in with an apiarist?' I said. 'I'm told they're the most unstressed people around.'

She examined me as she might a chipped tooth—worth saving, maybe, but a lot of work. 'Where would I find a landlord who'd let me get so far behind with the rent?'

'Well, you're helping me defraud the income tax people.' Saying that swung my mind back to John Singer. His tax records would be interesting. Maybe he owed a bundle and had decided to default.

'Income tax,' Hilde said. 'I'm looking forward to paying some, lots.'

I grunted. Youthful idealism is hard to take. 'How's your love life?' I was thinking of my big empty bed upstairs, the useless stirrings and the occasional dreams with unhappy endings.

'Lousy.' She stretched up for the ceiling; her small, hard breasts rose up under her shirt and I got a glimpse of her flat tennis player's stomach. 'There's a lecturer I fancy. Lovely guy with a bitch of a wife. Nothing doing.'

'Probably too old for you, anyway.'

'Mm, thirty at least.'

Ancient, I thought, *past it, ready for the monkey gland injections*. I left her to the television and went upstairs, thinking about her and Marion Singer and Ann Winter. Tenant, client, and what?

My bedroom was dusty and there were more coffee cups in it than in the kitchen. I made a nest of them and swore to take them down in the morning. The pile of paperbacks had toppled over on the dresser and knocked the transistor radio onto the floor. I picked it up and heard it rattle ominously when I shook it. I put it down, deciding to let the full force of that disaster wait until the following day.

45

In the morning I tramped virtuously down with the coffee cups but Hilde hadn't left the customary pot on the stove. I drank instant grumpily and leafed through the phone book until I found William A. Winter of Point Piper. After getting past a woman with strong public school vowels, I had Ann on the line.

'God,' she said. 'I'm hung.'

'Shocking. Any cops yet?'

'No, they'll be at the dump I expect. No-one much knows about the Travelodge here.'

'Bruce mentioned this wino on the tape, Leon. You said you knew him too. D'you know where I can find him?'

'He sleeps in a sort of chookhouse out in the back yard of a place in the street behind Bruce's. I don't know the number but you can't miss it. It's a three-storey terrace, free-standing, chunder-green.'

'Okay, thanks.'

'What's the time?' Her voice was blurry and she was having trouble hitting the hard consonants. Southern Comfort.

'Nine-twenty. Why?'

'At ten you'll find Leon on the steps of the Haworth Arms.' She spelled the word out.'

'I've read the book,' I said. 'I'll try there first. You okay?'

'I will be when I've had a shower and some coffee and a hair of the dog. When will I see you next?'

'What about Manny's tonight, at six, say?'

'Right.'

My parents had lived in Bronte some time before I was born. My sister remembers it; she says that that when they quarrelled he threatened to drown her at the beach. She'd just laugh at him and go off to the pub. It wasn't so different from what I remembered happening when we lived at Maroubra. I can remember my father walking with me along that big, empty Maroubra beach while my mother was in the pub.

I had more leisure for these pleasant thoughts on this drive to Bronte. It was a bright, mild day and the council workers carving up a section of Oxford Street were whistling. I drove through the cutting and past Bronte beach which is scaled right down from Bondi—the sand, the grass, the changing sheds, the lot—and up towards the Waverley cemetery where the dead are laid out in rows on a headland, eternally oriented towards New Zealand.

A jogger strained up the grade and took a rest leaning on one of the sandstone horse troughs outside the cemetery. It was a long time since a horse had taken a breather there. I drove down beside the cemetery to take a look at the water before I plunged into pubs and rundown, chunder-green boarding houses. The dark blue sea, white-flecked and streaked with deep greens and silvery patches, rolled away forever to the east. The waves were high and even, occasionally rolling over and dumping with deep, resonant crashes. The board riders still defied them, but the waves could wait.

I located the Haworth Arms in my *Guide to Sydney Pubs* and headed for it. The warm day wouldn't matter one way or the other to the step-sitters; their skins would be permanently tanned from years of walking the streets and sleeping rough. Leon, with a chookhouse to doss in, would be an aristocrat amongst them.

There were five of them on the steps, warriors of the bottle, who looked old but who probably weren't. I addressed myself to the most awake-looking, a character with grey hair to his shoulders and a face as seamed as W. H. Auden's.

'I'm looking for Leon,' I said.

'Ain't here. Got the price of a schooner, mate?'

I gave him a dollar and he put it carefully into the inside breast pocket of the ancient suit coat he wore.

'I heard he was always here.'

'S'right, but he ain't. First time in I dunno how long.' He turned to a small fat man who was rolling a cigarette out of what looked like cannibalised butts. 'Seen Leon, Clyde?' Clyde shook his head. I wondered if he thought that was worth a dollar, but he evidently didn't because he didn't look up. I carry a few cigarettes with me to prove that I've beaten the habit fair and square. I passed two across to Clyde, who put them cautiously into his makings tin.

'Ta. Leon's sick, probably, or dead.'

I jumped. 'Why d'you say that?'

'Stands to reason. He ain't here, usually means a man's sick or dead. Right, Stan?'

The man with the ploughed paddock face nodded. 'Right.'

I drove back to Henneberry's place and parked across the street. The sun hit the rounded white section of the flats, giving the building an exotic, Moorish look. I wondered how long it would take the landlord to re-let and decided it would depend on the carpet; he'd be slowed up if he had to replace it.

Life got a bit tougher in the streets further back. The houses were small and cramped; there was no view from here but some of the buildings actually grovelled down below street level as if emphasising the fact. The chunder-green joint stood out like an elephant among mice. It started about a foot back from the street and there was just enough room between the building and the fences on either side for a skinny cat to slip by.

I knocked on the front door gingerly. The disgusting green colour was everywhere and it had a slimy look as if it would come off on your hand. An enormously fat woman wearing a print dress and a crazily buttoned cardigan came to the door. She filled the doorway and when she spoke her three chins turned into four or five.

'I'd like to see Leon, please.'

She looked at me and two tears as big as grapes squeezed out of her eyes and began to traverse the fat.

'You can't,' she said. 'He bloody died last night.'

9

H^{ER} name was Rose Jenkins. She was a talker, and she invited me back to her kitchen, where she made tea I didn't drink. She gave it to me in great detail: she managed the boarding house in which there were fourteen roomers. Leon she let sleep in a lean-to out back for a nominal rent. Sometimes he'd come into the house to use the toilet; for the less serious calls of nature, he'd use the backyard. I was beginning to get a rounded-out picture of Leon.

I persuaded her to stop drinking tea and talking and show me the relevant scenes. The lean-to smelled bad. You could have called it airy and in winter it would be only marginally better than being out under a tree. There was a tattered mattress on the concrete floor with a heavy tweed coat, fashionable between the wars, thrown over it. The pillow was a pile of newspapers. The toilet was off a first-floor landing. Leon had come down from that level the short way, and his neck had been broken.

'Did anyone see the fall?' I asked.

Mrs Jenkins shook her head and the fat bounced and jiggled. 'No, none of them what lives in the back part of the house was home when it happened. Mr Brass come home at about eight and he found the poor soul there. He was all hunched up against the wall and terrible broken up, they said.'

'You didn't see him?'

She shook her head again and looked away from the stairs. I walked up them counting, thirteen in all. The toilet had a light burning inside it and some light seeped out through the cracked door. There was a light switch on the landing; I flicked it and a sixty- or seventy-five-watt bulb came on above the top stair. There was a threadbare but intact carpet outside the toilet and a runner in the same condition on the stairs.

I went back to the kitchen and asked Rose whether the landing light had been on yesterday in the afternoon and evening.

'Oh, yes,' she said. 'Some of me roomers are quite old, you know. They need the light.'

Then I asked her why she hadn't asked me for any identification and why she was talking so freely to me.

'Nothing would surprise me now,' she said.

'How's that?'

'They found quite a bit of money in Leon's room, in the mattress. The police, I mean. They wouldn't say how much, but someone said they filled a paper bag with it. I thought you were something to do with the money.'

I let her go on thinking it. I was thinking myself. A derelict with a bag full of money isn't unique; Griffo had had a few thousand in the bank when he died, and he'd been panhandling for years. Also, Leon wouldn't have been the first man to be murdered for the money in the mattress, but in those cases the murderer usually bothered to take the money with him or her. I was sweating in the warm, still air when I got back to the car and that made a drink seem like a good idea.

I found a pub within walking distance from where I'd parked and went in to do some more thinking over a middy. It had begun to look as if Mrs Singer had been on to something and that someone wasn't happy about information about John Singer being passed around. My enquiry seemed to be the likely link between the deaths of Henneberry and Leon if the latter wasn't an accident. I didn't think it was. Information, whatever it was, had, in this scenario, caused the deaths of two men. I didn't have the information myself but I was still looking for it and I had to face the fact that someone might object strenuously. Not for the first time I reflected that a hundred and twenty a day wasn't a good rate for getting dead, but there was no point in upping the fees. A thousand a day is still a poor deal.

True to my new code, I had just the one beer. Back at the car I looked across at the flats, which had lost their Hollywood Morocco air as the sun had moved on. The street was peaceful;

50

a couple of cars drifted by and a woman strolled along the pavement with a small child weaving around beside her. It was hard to believe that two murders had been committed within a stone's throw. Then I told myself I hadn't clinched that the way it needed to be clinched.

Back in College Street, I had the feeling that I was criss-crossing my tracks and not finding my way out of the woods. The cop at the desk was a survivor of the days when I used to visit Evans there, and he let me go up to Frank Parker's office without an escort. I admired Frank's cool even more when I saw how his working conditions shaped up when everyone was in. All four detectives were at their desks; there was a fug in the air and one of the cops was hitting a typewriter like an enraged child. Another was slamming filing cabinet doors as if it was his favourite indoor sport. Parker wasn't fazed; he had his head down and was annotating a typed sheet with a gold ballpoint pen. His shirt cuffs were folded neatly back, and under the nasty, flickering fluorescent light the scar on his arm stood out like an airstrip in the jungle. There were three phones within Parker's reach; one rang and he unerringly grabbed the right one. He looked up, saw me and nodded. He tucked the phone under his chin and pulled a sheet of paper towards him.

I leaned against a filing cabinet and congratulated myself that I didn't have to sit behind a desk covered with paper. Parker's paper problem was enormous and although he looked as if he had the stuff well organised, it was threatening to organise him. He put the phone down quietly, finished his note-making and folded his hands on top of the paper. He didn't wear any ring.

'Hardy,' he said. 'What a pleasure.'

'Busy, Frank?'

He smiled cautiously.

'Does anyone ever come to take any of this stuff away?' I asked.

'I don't think so. What can I do for you?'

'Making any progress on the Henneberry case?'

He riffled through some paper and pulled out a sheet with some of his neat ballpoint notes on it. 'I sent a policewoman to see the Winter girl. Haven't got her full report yet, but she says she didn't get anything interesting out of her. She doesn't seem to know a hell of a lot for someone who's going to be a doctor or whatever.'

'They're like that. It's pretty unhealthy in Bronte right now, isn't it?'

'What are you talking about?'

'Did you hear about Leon?'

'Oh, yeah, I heard about it.' He flip-flopped his hand across the desk. 'Down the stairs with a bump. So what?'

'Did you hear about the money in his mattress?'

'No.'

'I've seen those stairs. They're pretty gentle. Carpeted, too.' He grunted and lit a cigarette.

'I'd like to see the medical guff on Leon,' I said.

'Why?'

'It sounds to me like he was thrown down the stairs, not pushed—thrown. Wouldn't you say it took a pretty strong man to do Henneberry in?'

'Yes.'

'There's a connection between Henneberry and Leon.'

He blew out the smoke to where it could join up with the other smoke. 'What do I want with two murders?'

'Good murders,' I said. 'Original style. I can tell you that Henneberry saw Leon yesterday and they talked. I don't know what about, but there's a connection. If the case gets big you might need some help.' I prodded at the mountain of paper. 'Help, Frank. Administrative assistance.'

He looked at me shrewdly but I could feel his eagerness. Frank was ambitious, Frank liked action. He caressed the words. 'Administrative assistance,' he said.

'Right. I'm told Henneberry's people are big noises in the States.' That was stretching it a bit, but I was on a winning streak. 'There'll be pressure. This is a big case for you, Frank.'

'Let's go and look at the file,' he said.

Like everything else, police records are getting the computer treatment. Frank told me he'd done a computer course after

52

joining the force so the visual display terminal system was child's play to him. We went into a small room that contained six desks set up in front of small screens with typewriter-style keyboards mounted under them. Frank sat down and started punching buttons.

'The preliminary stuff should be here,' he said. 'The autopsy will be, because the technical boys know how to use the system.' There was a suggestion of contempt for people who didn't know how to use it. I nodded sagely and tried to look informed.

The greenish-grey screen suddenly filled with white print, which Frank scrutinised closely. He hit the buttons some more and the print rolled on.

'Multiple fractures,' he said. 'Skull in a couple of places, ribs.'

'Not there from a fall,' I said. 'No way.'

'Probably pissed,' he said, and hit another button. He read some more and looked up. 'Not pissed, not by his standards.'

'There you are. There's a light at the top of the stairs, too.'

'Looks funny.' He rubbed his chin and then jerked his hand away as if he was disciplining himself not to rub his chin. I wondered what he did for fun.

'It stinks,' I said. 'Someone's got to talk to all Leon's mates. He might have seen someone after he talked to Henneberry and passed something on. There's got to be a reason behind it.'

'You're a great talker, Hardy, but the obvious connection is with what you're working on, and you've told me bugger all about that.'

'All I know is that they talked, I don't know what about. I'm in the dark, too.' That wasn't quite true; I had a few indications and the ashram to look into, but what I said next was the whole truth. 'Look, Frank, I'll tell you the lot in a day or so, as I promised. Shit, I'll want you in the minute anything breaks, if it does. I don't want to go up against the Bronte strangler all on my own—I'll want dogs, horses, gas, the lot.'

'All right.' He unfolded his long legs from under the desk and stood up, ready for action. 'I'll put in a request for someone to work on that mess and I'll get out on the street.'

For a minute I thought he was going to thank me, but that

would've been asking a bit too much. Cops like being on the street, of course, the good ones because they feel they're doing something useful out there and the bad ones because of their lubricity—for the free women with the drinks and food thrown in. But Frank Parker didn't look about to slide from good to bad.

'I'll be in touch,' I said.

'No more bodies, Hardy. Please, no more bodies.'

10

THE ashram in Salisbury Street was a converted car show-room or something similar. It was long and low and had a big window onto the street. This had been blanked out by yellow paint; the whole place was painted yellow, not the bright, buttercup version but a deeper colour shading down towards orange. There was no sign on the building to indicate its purpose, but on either side of the wide doors were posters. They were blowups of a photograph of a weird scene and I stared at it for a full minute without comprehension. It looked like a moonscape with a Hitler youth rally going on, except that the faithful wore loincloths. The poster had the word 'GIVE' in capitals above and below the picture.

The joint was painted yellow inside too; at least, as far as I got, which was only into a small, partitioned-off reception room. There was a picture on the wall of a scrawny little number with no chin and rimless glasses. He looked to me a lot like Heinrich Himmler, but I could have been free-associating with the picture outside. An old woman wearing yellow robes reproached me for flippancy when I asked the name of the guru. I asked for Brother Gentle and she told me he wasn't in. I asked for his second-in-command, and she said that there was no command structure in the ashram. I gathered that she was minding the fort while all the able-bodied devotees were out filling the money bins. I left a card and said I'd call back. Her wrinkled old face arranged itself in a smile and she said something in one of the many languages I don't understand.

'What does that mean?' I asked.

'May the sun fill your heart.'

'And yours,' I said.

I found some old shorts and a towel in the car, changed and

went for a swim. It was cold but the surf was low and I ploughed along, telling myself that giving up cigarettes was the smartest thing I'd ever done. In sheer physical moments like that I almost believed it. After the swim I jogged gently along the beach in the sun; the sand was hard-packed and substantial and I stretched out trying to get some bounce into my forty-year-old style. Off to the west the buildings and the foreign-looking trees had a temporary, painted-on appearance, as if a big wind could get up in the centre of Australia and push the whole lot into the sea.

I went to sleep on the sand and woke up with a start. I'd been dreaming about a wave. It started as a little fellow just spanking the water's edge, then it went back, rolled in again and got bigger each time. The last time it was really big, rolling over the sand towards the pavilion.

I went for another swim and then sat watching the movement of the tide. The beach emptied around me; where bodies had been, there were now just impressions in the sand casting low shadows. Soon the water would come up and smooth them out. The beach got a clean slate every day, unlike people.

Manny was polishing glasses when I got to the coffee bar. He held one up. 'Drink?'

'All right. Thanks.'

He poured two hefty tumblers of yellowish fluid. I took a swig. It was raw and fruity.

'Make it myself,' he said. 'Very bad about Bruce.'

'Very bad.'

'Very dangerous place, Sydney.'

I grunted, wondering what other dangerous places he knew.

'The police were here,' he said.

I looked up at the shelf where the cassettes were stacked. He shook his head. 'Didn't tell them about that.'

'Why not?'

He finished off his wine, if that's what it was, in a gulp. 'Where I come from we have a saying—don't trust your mother or your sister or your brother, they might be sleeping with a policeman.'

I nodded and took a conservative sip. 'How did you get

involved with this? I mean, Ann and Bruce?'

'Bruce came in for coffee and we got talking. I said there weren't too many young men around like him, made strong. They're all, what is it—weedy? Or fat. But Bruce, he was strong.'

'Yeah, he was.'

'We arm-wrestled a couple of times.' He looked me over dubiously. 'You wanna try it?'

'No thanks.' His biceps and neck muscles stretched the ribbing on his T-shirt. 'Who won the wrestling?'

'Bout a draw. I used to want to be a writer. Long time ago. Bruce talked about his writing and Ann, she's a writer too isn't she?'

'Sort of,' I said. 'So you helped them?'

He shrugged and poured himself another slug. 'Have another?'

'No, thanks, I'll go steady. I'm expecting Ann in soon.'

His moustache seemed to droop even more and his eyes and mouth pursed up tightly. 'You going to work with Ann?'

'No. Why?'

'Should,' he said. 'Drug scene here is real bad.'

'Not my line,' I said and, saying it, remembered what my line was. I pulled out my photographs of Singer and handed them to him. 'Ever see this bloke?'

He looked at the pictures carefully, first at one and then the other. He seemed to be analysing the images, judging them, but by what criteria I had no idea.

'Sorry, Mr Hardy, never seen him. What'd he do?'

Before I could answer, Ann Winter came dodging between the tables. She was wearing the same clothes as she had the day before but her hair was shining with Point Piper shampoo.

''Lo Cliff, 'lo Manny.' She sat down near us and began to roll a smoke. Manny slid away towards his coffee machine and I moved across to sit opposite her. She looked up from the makings to smile at me as if she liked crows' feet and broken noses. Maybe she did.

'How were the cops?' I asked.

'Cop,' she said. 'Interesting.' She ran her tongue along the edge of the paper and completed the cigarette. Manny put a coffee down in front of her and lit the cigarette in a series of nice fluid movements. There was something threatening about his combination of good manners, bulk and deft movement. Ann bobbed her head at him and went on talking through her smoke.

'She's young and she studied sociology. We had a good talk. It was a bit like a seminar, really.'

I finished the wine in a swallow. 'Sociology?' I said.

'Yes. Majored in it, same department as me. She was very understanding.'

I was used to cops who majored in football with sub-majors in Holdens and snooker. It looked as if Frank Parker had some classy help in the field.

'What did you tell her?'

'Nothing much. What do I know? I didn't mention you.'

'Take your tapes?'

'No, I explained that they were my research material and she said that was okay.'

Understanding is right, I thought. It seemed a rational way to deal with an intelligent person like Ann Winter. Frank Parker was acting pretty shrewdly with me; perhaps we were entering a time when the cops suited their approach to the subject. I wondered what the appropriate approach would be for the person who had disembowelled Bruce Henneberry. I looked down and realised that I'd automatically taken Ann's tobacco and had started to roll a cigarette. I finished it and tucked it away in the pouch.

'How long did you smoke for?'

'Twenty-five years.' That was true, and it meant that I'd started about the time she was born. She nodded and puffed.

'And it still bothers you?'

'Not much. Just when I need to think.'

She laughed. 'It must bother you all the time, then.'

'Not really. I do a lot of sitting in cars looking around, walking down streets with people carrying money—babysitting, really.'

'This isn't babysitting.' She drained the coffee and pulled hard on her cigarette. 'What about Leon?' The way she said the name was an accusation. 'You know he's dead?'

'Yeah, I know.'

'Maybe I should give that cassette to the police.' She stubbed the butt out, hard. 'Only I can't because you've got it.'

'Take it easy,' I said. 'I'll give it to them myself in a day or so if I don't come up with something. I promised Parker.'

'Constable Reynolds had a word or two to say about him.'

I invited her to tell all, but she wouldn't. I asked her what she'd heard about Leon.

'Just that he died. Oh, yes. I'm invited to his wake tonight.'

'His what?'

'Wake. He left some money and a note that said he wanted to have a wake. The woman who manages the house found the note and word got around. I got asked through a girl who fixes up the old men.'

'Fixes them how?'

'Fucks them, of course, or gets them as close as she can. D'you want the details? She . . .'

'No, I don't want the details, but I do want to go to the wake.'

'Why?'

I shrugged. 'Something might happen, someone might say something interesting. Will you take me? Where is it?'

She looked at me and didn't reply. I reminded myself that she was trained to observe, judge and report on people, to classify and quantify them. I tried to look responsible and intelligent, disinterested and analytical.

'Why are you looking like that?' she asked.

'Like what?'

'Your face has gone stiff. You look like a moron.'

'I was trying to look serious. I want to go to the wake.'

'You're supposed to bring a bottle.'

I nodded. 'I'll bring two. Yes?'

'Okay. Let's go and eat first; we'll need a foundation for the grog.'

We ate Lebanese food at a place on the Parade. It wasn't as good as it is in Darlinghurst, but it was better than in Glebe. I bought a bottle of brandy and a flagon of wine at a pub and we had a little of the wine just to help the food down. During the meal I noticed her pent-up nervousness for the first time. Her hands were never still; she did things with her hair, shredded the flat bread, smoked. It was as if she was afraid to be still, afraid that it would make her some sort of target. When she started tracing patterns in the hoummos with a match I reached over and moved her hand away.

'Your people must be loaded with that house and all,' I said. 'Why aren't you off ski-ing somewhere or learning to make stained-glass windows?'

She took it the right way and grinned. 'Somehow I just can't seem to get the idea of filling up my life that way.'

'Who's got the millions?'

'Both of 'em. His dough is from land development and that, bit grubby. Hers is old money from the land—New England. I've got an older brother just like him and a twin sister just like her, so they're happy. They leave me alone.'

'Do you enjoy this, the field work?'

She frowned. 'Sometimes I hate it, sometimes it's okay. They're an awful mess, the girls, but they're alive, at least. They're tough and brave. It's bloody confusing.'

'How do you mean?'

'Well, you know, I've got all the middle-class, educated views on things like peace and that. But what these kids would be really good at would be a war. In a way they need a war.'

'Or a revolution?'

'Yeah, but . . .'

'But they'd get screwed in a war or a revolution just the same.'

'That's right.'

'What'll you do when you're Dr Winter?'

She shrugged. 'Don't know. It's two years away at least. That's too far ahead to worry about. I've learned that much around here.'

She was right there. Only the comfortable and secure look and plan two years ahead.

'I suppose you think I'm a phoney,' she said. 'Slumming it up around Bondi with Point Piper to go back to?'

I was surprised and concerned. I didn't think that and I didn't want her to think that I did. 'No,' I said firmly. 'I don't think you're a phoney. You're doing a job and you can probably do it better if you can scrub the shit off once in a while. That was the theory in the army.'

'When were you in the army?'

'Long time ago, in Malaya.'

'Can't see you as a soldier.'

'I wasn't very good.'

'Why not?'

I hesitated. I didn't usually talk about Malaya, although I thought about it a good deal. Something made me willing to talk about it now—maybe it was her interviewing technique. But she had that ability some women have of making you feel like the most important thing around at the moment. I'd met it before and I fell for it every time.

'I was very scared,' I said slowly. 'But I was more scared of showing that I was scared. I did stupid things, risked other people's lives. Also I was erratic, unreliable.'

'Did you care about the cause? Fighting against the Chinese communists, wasn't it?'

'That's right. No, I didn't give a bugger. Didn't understand it at all. I believed what I was told.'

'That says a lot about you.'

'What?'

'You don't believe what you're told any more, do you? That's your job—not believing what you're told.'

I could see what she meant, and there was something in it. Maybe I was still an anti-soldier, but since then I'd had a bit more experience at the differences between what you're told and what is—with Cyn, for example. I let that stay private and we sat there for a few minutes quietly. She smoked, but placidly, for her.

I poured us a bit more wine, which still left us a very respectable amount to take to the wake.

'Two men have died since you started looking for this guy,' she said. 'What's his name again?'

'Singer.'

'Singer. Two dead men. What does that mean, for Christ's sake?'

'Could be anything. Bruce might have stumbled onto how Singer got to be dead, if he is dead. Or he might have found out that he's not dead. I just can't get past that point.'

'If he's alive, why isn't he around enjoying that yacht?'

'And that wife.'

'Attractive wife?'

'Pretty good.'

'Strikes me you ought to find out a bit more about the wife.'

'Yeah, and about Brother Gentle and McLeary and the other operator around here whose name I don't even know.'

'You're going to be busy. Do you still want to go to the wake?'

She gathered her things up and looked around for the bill. I took it, thinking that Mrs Singer would pay it and wondering where she was eating tonight and with whom. Ann was right; I didn't know nearly enough about the lady. She'd charmed me, I knew that, but was she the kind to provoke a suicide or a murder? Ann looked at me impatiently. She was the kind not to be slowed down or kept waiting.

'Yes', I said, 'I want to go to the wake.'

11

THERE were a few extra lights burning in the boarding house, but no extra cars in the street. It wasn't that sort of a party. I went through the security routine I'd developed for party-going many years before—wallet locked in the glove box, car keys tucked up underneath the vehicle, mad money folded small and wedged down in a pocket. Ann watched me incredulously.

'Where's your gun?' she said.

'In the car. Reckon I'll need it?'

'No. Got the grog?'

The front door was open and we walked down the passage towards the back of the house where I could hear soft, mournful music. The kitchen was crowded with men and women, and Mrs Jenkins sat at the table with those big, fat tears rolling down. Behind her a wizened-up monkey of a man was working his piano accordion and moaning out 'Kevin Barry'. He was very drunk. The music was all right, but he hit and missed the notes like a housewife on *Amateur Hour*. Some of the others joined in when the words came back to them, but they weren't much better.

I sat the bottles down on the sink, got two paper cups and poured two hefty whacks of the brandy. I handed one to Ann and when I turned back for mine the bottle had gone. I sipped the drink and studied the company. Mostly, the guests bore the marks of alcohol but not the broken veins of the whisky drinker or the gross bellies of the ten-schooner-a-day-folk. These were metho drinkers, eaten away to the bone by the stuff, or port people with their metabolisms shot to pieces by the rushes of alcohol and sugar. Half of them were thin, with the sugar-loaded blood of uncontrolled diabetics—they'd piss a lot and their noses would run from the colds they'd be a prey to and sex would be a distant memory. But tonight they were happy; tonight they were on plonk and beer and spirits and Leon's death had given them a focus, a target for the emotions and energies which were usually concentrated on the next bottle.

I whispered to Ann, 'Do you know any of these people?'

'A few. See that woman in pink? How old do you think she is?'

'Sixty?'

'Forty.'

'Jesus.'

I finished my brandy and a man leaning against the sink produced the bottle with a courtly flourish.

'A refill, squire?'

'Okay. Thanks'.

He poured me a judicious one and half-filled his own mug. He raised it.

'Lucky Leon,' he exclaimed.

'Why do you say that?'

He dropped his head on his chest. His hand shook, but he was an expert at keeping fluid in a vessel held in a shaking hand. He was wearing cast-off clothes that were too big for him and heavy, broken shoes that had been expensive and stylish fifteen years before. He said something, but a burst of clapping at the end of a song drowned him out. I bent down to hear better and his smell almost floored me. He had it all, layers of body odour, urine and the rotten meat smell of decaying teeth.

'A clean exit to a better world,' he said.

'Do you live here, Mr . . .?'

'Montefiore. I have, not now. Are you making enquiries?'

'God, is it that obvious? Yes, I am in a way, but I'm also here to pay my respects.'

'You've done it.' He held up the bottle. 'Leon would have been pleased to know that such a quality beverage was being served at his wake.'

'Did you know him well, Mr Montefiore?'

'Edgar. Yes, quite well.'

I looked around the room. Ann was talking to the woman in

pink, who was swaying on her chair. A great lock of red hair had fallen across her face and she was trying to push it back, but getting less interested. Mrs Jenkins had brought out a cigarette-rolling machine and Ann was making them. A few people around the table were watching with critical, greedy eyes.

I turned back to Edgar, who was filling his mug again. The high-quality beverage was getting to him because he was rocking slightly and his bloodshot eyes were glassy.

'Edgar, do you happen to know what Leon had been doing the day he died?'

'Doing?' he slurred. 'Didn't do anything, old chap. Started off at the Haworth and went on from there.'

'Where did he get the money?'

'Pension cheque and . . . donations.'

'Street donations, or did he knock on doors?'

'Had a theory, Leon. Principle really—charity begins at home. Didn't care too much for foreign relief in India, if you take my meaning. Used to call in where he saw signs of charity being dispensed and claim his share. Had a wonderful line of chat.'

'You don't know specifically where he went that day?'

'No, sir. Saw him in the street in the afternoon.' He tipped up his mug. 'Do you know, I think he was very close to sober. Disgraceful, I said. Pale, he was, and shaking. Suppose he was sick. Suppose that's how he fell. Negotiated those stairs myself many times, drunk as a lord, never fell.'

'It could have been that,' I said. But I was thinking of the 'GIVE' poster outside the ashram and wondering what it took to make a confirmed drunkard sober in the late afternoon.

The booze was reaching the celebrants' motor centres; the accordionist had put his instrument down and was sitting quietly, smoking one of Ann's cigarettes. One man was slumped in a corner, snoring. The woman in pink stared fixedly at a paper cup in front of her and poured small amounts into it from the variety of bottles on the table. The front of Rose Jenkins's dress was soaked with tears or wine or both; she was talking to Ann, who smiled and nodded in reply. A tall, thin man slid down against the wall and the beer bottle in his hand smashed on the cement floor. No-one took any notice.

Edgar held the brandy bottle up to the light and read from the label in a loud, stagey voice. 'Product of Australia,' he intoned. He closed his eyes as if great pain had gripped him. 'Australia. God.'

I looked across and caught Ann's eye. She nodded and patted Mrs Jenkins's vast upper arm.

'Thanks for coming, dear,' the woman said mournfully.

We went towards the door, stepping over the man in the corner, who was sitting oblivious in a pool of beer. Halfway down the passage, a question occurred to me and I told Ann to wait while I hurried back to the kitchen. Rose had her nose in a cup of brandy that Edgar had given her; he was leaning over her and touching his fingertip to her ear in a parody of sexual play.

'Mrs Jenkins,' I said. 'Were there any strangers in the house yesterday?'

'Stranger?'

'Yes; anyone wearing yellow, for example?'

'White, did you say? No, yellow—no-one in yellow.' She hiccoughed and wheezed.

'Was there someone in white?'

She slurped the brandy. 'Don't remember. Go 'way.'

Edgar Montefiore put his index finger with its black-rimmed nail into her ear. I went away. Back in the hall, Ann was pinned back against the wall by a big man with an Ulster accent who was haranguing her about Ireland. He wasn't drunk or sober and he was pressing closer, making the attack physical as well as verbal. I put my hand on Ann's shoulder and gently eased him back. I had an elbow ready for his ribs if he turned nasty, but he said something uncomplimentary about Protestants and moved off towards the grog.

The encounter upset Ann more than I'd have expected. She was pale and the shoulder muscles under my hand were knotted and tense as we went out to the street.

'I hate that,' she said fiercely.

'What?'

'Needing to have a man around to rescue me.'

66

There was nothing to say to that—chivalry is chauvinism, protection is paternalism. She was five foot ten and weighed ten stone; with tae kwon do, she'd be a terror on the mat. But tae kwon do is no good if you're upset and, like it or not, that's how most women react to a physical threat. I've talked it over with them, especially Hilde, and they argue that male violence makes them react that way. So they win the argument and still lose the fight. I took my hand away.

'Did you have an interesting time?' Her voice was edged with irony and hostility.

'Yes. You?'

'Poor cows,' she said. 'I asked Pearl, she was the one in the pink, about your Mr Whatsit. She reckons she knows a lot about them, the Singers. I think she meant the wife, too.'

'What's her name, that woman?'

'Well, she's going by the name of Spenser right now, I think. She's had other names. Names are a bit fluid in this crowd. Some people have a couple. For the pension, you know?'

'I've heard of it. I thought it got stamped out.'

'No way.'

'I should talk to her.'

'Not much point now; she's too pissed.'

'Would you go back and ask? There'd be some money in it for her.'

She shrugged. 'If you like.' She turned and walked away very straight, the way you do when you've had enough drinks to care about how you walk.

The car was up ahead. I took a few very straight steps and suddenly there was a pain in my arm and I wondered why. Then there was a whole lot of pain, a flood of it, and some very loud noises. My feet left the ground and my head swooped down towards it and there was nothing after that.

12

WHEN I could feel things again, I wished I couldn't. I was lying still and yet moving, there was a constant sound and also a deep silence and my head felt as if it was flapping loose and I couldn't move my body. I was very confused. After a while I worked out that I was on the back seat of a big car. My hands and legs were tied, my shoulders were on the seat but my head was hanging half off it. I wriggled and thrashed until I got some support for my head. It still hurt, but at least it felt attached to my body.

'Hey,' I said, feebly. 'Hey!' I twisted and pushed until I forced my head up far enough to see two heads and two pairs of shoulders. I could excuse the driver for not responding; you need to concentrate on your driving when you've got someone trussed up on the back seat, but it was just plain rude of the other guy to ignore me. Still, that's what he did and kept on doing. It was dark and I couldn't see much out of the windows except the odd light. To judge by noises I wasn't in the city, but I wasn't on the Nullarbor Plain either.

I fought to control the panic that the thought of an unsolicited trip to the country with strangers is apt to bring on. I tried to think of any reasons why anyone should be thinking of a shallow grave in the bush for me. There was nothing pressing. I thought I could risk a little resistance so I drew my legs up to my chest and pushed them back hard to thump against the door. A hand came over with a big black gun in it. The metal slammed down hard on my shinbone and I yelped.

'Don't,' a voice said.

I closed my eyes and tried for some of that displacement of body and spirit that Jack London wrote about in *The Jacket*. His hero travelled in time, fought off pirates and fired flintlocks at circling Indians from the cover of a wagon. I think he got girls every time. Nothing happened and I began to worry about Ann. Was she in a car, too, or had she been around the corner when they took me? Then I thought: *Why,* again, *and who?* Good questions, no answers.

I could see the moon through the window but I couldn't tell the time by the moon. Who can? The car stopped, turned and followed what felt like a rough, unmade road for a while and then it stopped again. The man with the gun got out, the car moved forward a few yards, stopped and he got back in. Private property.

I bounced and rolled around on the seat and tried to work out how far we were going from the road. I couldn't; it might have been one mile or six. When the car stopped, the gunman opened the back door and looked at me. The interior light was on and I looked back: he had a meaty face with a dimple in his chin. He would have been handsome in an overblown way except for small, close-set eyes that gave him a slightly piggy look. When he was satisfied that I was still tied up, he pulled my legs and tumbled me out inelegantly onto the ground. He put his gun away in his belt.

'He here yet?' he asked.

Another voice behind me said, 'No. What'll we do with him?'

'How long?'

'Morning, probably. early.'

'Shit.'

I looked around as best I could with my face half in the dirt. I could see white painted fences, trees and the dark shapes of buildings, one very large. I spat out the dirt and sniffed the clean country air. I groaned, thinking that they might put me on a bed if they thought I was hurt. The car door slammed and I saw the feet and legs of the car driver come into view.

'What's the trouble, Rex?' he asked. He had a soft American accent, southern or something. It wasn't the voice of a humanitarian; more a 'kick him in the head' voice than a 'lay him gently on the bed' one.

'No trouble,' Rex said. He was the gunman and the weapon

in his belt looked like a nine-millimetre Browning, which is a lot of gun when your target is tied up like corned silverside. He pulled me up to my feet and I tried to grin at him.

'Think you'll need the gun, Rex?'

For an answer he hooked my feet out from under me and I fell heavily. It had been a dry winter and the ground was hard; now my shoulder hurt as well as my shin. I decided that I didn't like Rex.

'We'll put him in the squash court,' he said. He kicked me lightly in the ribs.

'Crawl, smartarse. Over there.'

I lay still, so he kicked me again harder and I crawled. It's hard to crawl when you're tied up like that; things stick into you and hurt. I got a cramp in the calf after a few yards and stopped. I felt his shoe again and moved on. It wasn't far, maybe less than a hundred yards, but my clothes were badly ripped and there was a lot of skin missing from me when I got there.

The driver and Rex had followed my progress, chatting chummily. At one point, at a pause for breath and to respond to a boot-delivered change in direction, I got a look at the driver. He wore white overalls and sported a heavy, dark beard. He was built strong and wide and looked like he could do a few useful things besides drive cars. At the end of the crawl the driver pulled out a bunch of keys and unlocked a door. Rex got hold of some shirt and flesh and pulled and pushed me over a low step; then he gave me one of those funny little kicks he was so good at and I pitched over onto a hard wooden floor.

They closed the door and it was very dark. I propped myself up against the wall and checked for serious injuries a limb at a time. I seemed to be in working order, although a lot of the normal movements hurt like hell. There were no windows in the room and I edged my way around the walls, feeling for a light switch with my head and shoulders. I found it and turned it on with my chin, but no light resulted. That was a disappointment. I squatted down again and told myself that a big house like this, and that shape had been really big, would have a master switch to turn off the light in the outbuildings. It was only natural; it wasn't a direct strike at Hardy.

The squash court was like a coffin. The floor was made of sanded, tightly-packed boards and the walls were smooth. I tried to remember what a court looked like in the light and couldn't. I'd never played the game, which seemed to me like a barbarity designed solely to make people sweat. I assumed there were lines painted on the floor, but there were no cupboards, no fittings, no racquets left lying about. I was wearing jeans and a denim shirt, desert boots and socks; it wasn't cold but it felt as if it could get cold, and that's nearly as bad. However I positioned myself it was impossible to sleep—I lost consciousness a few times, that's all.

I watched the light seep in around the edges of the door as the morning broke. I'd been wrong about the lack of windows; there was a skylight shaded by a tree. Enough light came in to show me the lines on the floor and wall; somehow, in that grey light, the room felt even more menacing than it had in the dark. I'd said a lot of unkind things about squash in my time, and I had the nasty feeling that squash was fighting back.

Just to show some spirit and get the blood flowing, I started battering the door with my shoulders and shouting. The driver came to the door and rapped on it.

'Shut up!' His intonation made it worse—he didn't really care whether I shut up or not. He said it contemptuously, and I slumped back down on the floor.

I panicked a bit then. I'd heard about a man who took two sleeping pills and some scotch when he got on a plane to London and who slept most of the way with his arm in the same poor circulation position. His arm was paralysed for a month as a result. My arms were stiff and sore behind me and I thought I was losing feeling in my hands. I battered and shouted some more, louder.

Rex opened the door. He was freshly showered and shaved; he smelled of after-shave and coffee. I hated him as much as I have ever hated anyone, which is a lot. He gestured with the gun for me to move back.

'What's wrong?' he said.

'I think my arms are paralysed. Pinched nerve or something.'

'Bullshit.'

'I've lost feeling in my hands.'

I could see him thinking it over. Does it matter? he was wondering. I wondered too; if it didn't matter that meant that my feeling things in my hands or anywhere else, wasn't part of the plan. I tried to keep my voice calm.

'I don't know what you want with me. Information, I suppose. If I'm paralysed I'd just as soon be dead and I won't tell anyone a fucking thing, whatever you do.'

'How're your legs?' He was just the hired help and now he had to make decisions. Life is so unfair.

'Sore and stiff. You put in a good boot. But it's the arms I'm worried about.'

He looked around the room carefully. Then he nodded and took a Swiss army knife out of his pocket, the kind that has a shifting spanner and a cross-cut saw on it.

'Lie down on your belly.'

I did and he put the muzzle of the gun in my ear while he sawed away with the knife. I screamed when my arms came free. At first I thought he'd cut me, but it was just the blood moving and a cramp gripping a muscle. But by the time I'd sat up and swivelled around, he had gone.

I moved my arms gently, massaging, stretching and bending until the feeling got back near normal. All the joints worked, the arms turned in their sockets, the elbows bent. But it took an age to get my legs free; the knots were tight and my fingers were sloppy. When I finished I had complete movement, it was 8.15 am and I had seven feet of hard, thin cord to play with.

I coiled the rope around my waist under my shirt and waited. At nine am I urinated near the door and most of it ran out. At nine-thirty there was some swearing outside and the door was unlocked. Rex was there with his trusty Browning, but the piss had produced some mud outside and he'd got it on his nice clean drill trousers.

'You filthy bastard,' he said.

'What'd you expect me to do? Piss in my mouth?'

He kept the gun steady and sneaked a look down at his slacks. Dry cleaning job, definitely.

'I oughter brain you for this.' His face went dark with anger and he lost a good bit of the slightly overweight elegance I'd credited him with. I felt better and gave him some more.

'It's only piss. Shouldn't stain if you get 'em off quick and give 'em a good soak. Get them off now.'

He looked ready to explode but a voice hailed him from behind. He drew in a deep, cooling-off breath.

'Get up. Try anything funny and I'll shoot you.'

I got up and walked stiffly to the door; I took a long step over the puddle and gave Rex a grin. He prodded me hard in a very tender rib with the gun.

'The house. Move!'

We tramped up a wide brick path to the house. The shapes of the previous night became identifiable buildings—a big garage, something that looked like a stable, a greenhouse. The property was a big place; the white fences ran up over a hill in one direction and the pasture flowed on uninterruptedly in another direction until it met the bush.

The house was Australian baronial, a huge affair, two-storeyed with a wide, white pillared verandah right around. There was a lot of sandstone in its construction and a good deal of timber and glass. Old timber, cedar and jarrah. It was a nineteenth-century house, a wool fortune house.

A fresh-looking Toyota Land Cruiser was parked near it; that made me check for other transportation in case I'd be doing some more travelling. I could see the rear end of a Volvo sticking out of the garage and nothing else. There were plenty of horses around. No light aircraft or helicopters.

We went up some steps to a door at the side of the house. Rex yelled, 'Tal!' twice and the driver opened the door. He was still wearing overalls, still looking useful.

'Billiard room,' Tal said.

We marched through several connecting rooms which seemed to have no function except as places to arrange furniture in. We went down a passage to where a leather-padded, studded door stood open. Tal went on ahead and said, 'He's here.'

The room was big and filled with light from a row of high-set windows; it was wood-panelled with two billiard tables, a dart board, some sporting prints on the walls and a bar. It had a sheep-roasting fireplace at one end. A man was bending over one of the tables, lining up a shot with the rapt concentration of an addict. He shot smoothly but missed. Then he straightened up and looked at me. I looked back. He was tall and thin with grey hair brushed severely back. He had the sort of grooved face that comes from dieting and his clothes—blue shirt, grey trousers and the vest of a three-piece suit—hung loosely on him as if he'd lost weight since they were bought or made. His small moustache didn't suit his rugged face. He chalked his cue with hands that looked well cared for but that hadn't always been so.

'Hardy,' he said.

'Right. Who're you?'

'You don't need to know.' He waved the cue expressively as if that dismissed the question and bent over the table again.

'I'm impressed,' I said. 'I'm impressed by your big house and your helpers and your billiard room. Squash court, too. Great setup. What's your interest in me?'

He shot again and missed again.

'You're not lined up right,' I said.

'What?'

'Your arse is off line. Swivel your hips a bit and get in line with the ball.'

He swung the cue and smashed its light end down on my shoulder. The wood splintered and I got a sharp pain to add to my dull, throbbing ones.

'Don't play the smartarse with me. I've seen better men than you off, right off. Understand?'

I rubbed the shoulder and nodded. His face was flushed and his thin body seemed stretched tight with the anger—short fuse, poor control, high blood pressure. Bad health risk, a 'D' life, as I'd have said in my insurance days. They had been boring, dispiriting days but right then they had a kind of attraction.

'What're you doing poking your nose around in Bondi?' he said.

'Working,' I said. 'I'm . . .'

'I know what you are, a small-time, shit-eating private investigator.' He made it sound bad, worse than it is. 'Who are you working for?'

I shook my head. 'Can't tell you that. Ethics of the profession.'

'Ethics,' he sneered. He was a good sneerer and the moustache looked better when he sneered. 'Look at you, you're a mess. How can it be worth it?' He sat down in a leather armchair and crossed his legs. His socks and shoes were black. Silk and leather, very pricey.

'Make me a drink, Rex.'

Rex moved over to the bar and got busy with the bottles. I turned a little and saw that Tal had a small gun out. I had two guns, one in Glebe and one in Bronte. Rex brought a nice tall scotch and soda across and handed it to his boss, who didn't thank him. He sipped the drink with a bit more than appreciation. At first glance he looked pretty good for an oldster, but on closer inspection there were signs of decay. He wasn't really that old, not more than sixty, but the grey hair was thin in spots and his colour wasn't good. The blue shirt lent it some life but there was something strange about his skin, as if it was trying to turn grey.

'Tell you what I'll do,' he said. 'I'll guess and you can nod, you don't have to say a word. No-one can say that you said anything, perfectly true.' He was trying for a pally tone but I didn't respond. 'It's got to be that Singer bitch, or Mac. Which one? Just give me a nod and I'll do the rest. You don't even have to tell us what you're doing.'

I watched him drink some more scotch and didn't say a thing.

'I'll pay you for your time. What d'you say?'

I didn't believe a word of it. It was as weak as a vicar's shandy. I believed him more when he was boasting and threatening.

'Sorry,' I said.

'You think you're tough?' He took a big drink and spilled a few drops on his vest. 'I could let Rex have you to himself in that squash room for a while.'

'I wouldn't mind,' I said.

'Rex and Tal together. How'd you like that?'

'Not as much.'

'You've been worked over once—what do you want, for Christ's sake?'

I didn't answer him. It seemed that my only chance lay in his uncertainty as to who I was working for. It was abduction already, guns were in view and he boasted of having killed men before. I believed him. But apparently he wouldn't kill me until he had sorted out who he was hitting at if he hit me. Maybe I was finished anyway, but they wouldn't kill me here, and I might get a chance on the way to wherever they would do it.

'You're fuckin' stupid!' The old rough side of him was showing now, the street side, maybe the gaol side. He finished the drink and for a minute I thought he was going to ask for another. That would have been hard on me, because I was feeling bad about the drink. I wanted one very badly, more for the wetness than the alcohol. I'd have settled for water. But I had a half-formed plan on that and I just clamped my jaw shut and tried to look resolute. He didn't ask for another scotch but I could tell he wanted it.

He got up. 'All right, Rex, sling him back in the box and let him think about it. Don't break his neck. Tal, I've got to go to town.'

Rex turned me around with a prod of the gun. I gave the broken end of the billiard cue a quick kick and it skittered across the planks. Rex jumped and prodded me again, Tal swore and the lord of the manor spun around as if he'd heard a shot. They were a very nervy bunch.

'Tonight, Hardy,' the boss man said. 'Or we'll put you in a hole.'

13

B^{ACK} in the box, I reflected on the little I'd learned from the encounter with the bad billiard player. Garth Green had mentioned someone else, apart from Singer and McLeary, who had a piece of the action on the beaches, and this looked like him. Those eastern suburbs enterprises must have been coining money, because this was a million-dollar setup. Apparently, though, all was not tranquil in that little world.

I worried about Ann Winter and about the fact that I couldn't see how all this action that had broken loose around me connected with John Singer, presumed dead. Rex didn't look like the Bronte ripper, either, but you never can tell. I wondered where I was, then I wondered if I'd ever know.

I heard a car start up and drive off—the Volvo. That took Tal and Mr Big away, and left Rex and who knew how many more. I started kicking the door. There was a bit of give in it and kicking made a satisfactory noise, although there was no hope at all of breaking it down. After five minutes' kicking, Rex's voice broke through the racket.

'Stop that fuckin' noise. What're you playing at?'

'Tongue swollen,' I croaked. 'Going to choke. Water.'

'Bullshit.'

'Something wrong.' I strangled and mangled my voice. 'Choking on it. Water, please.'

I heard his footsteps go back towards the house and I unwound the cord. I tied knots in one end, doubling them, until I had about five feet to swing and two feet in a hard, knobbly ball. I swung and cracked it a few times experimentally. I took a bead on the line on the wall and didn't miss by much.

The footsteps came back and a key turned in the door. I stood back a bit and let him come in; he had a plastic jug in one hand

and the gun in the other. He took his eye off me for a split second while he put the jug down. I stepped forward and lashed the rope at him. The ball got him squarely in the eye, which was my first piece of luck for quite some time. He yelped and raised the gun, but I was in close by then, chopping at his hand. The gun skidded across the smooth boards. He only had one eye to work with, but he was game; he rushed, trying to butt me back to the wall, but I sidestepped and kicked at his legs. He went down, jumped up fast and came in swinging. One punch landed on the shoulder the billiard cue had hit, and I bellowed with the pain. I walked through two punches and smashed a hard right to the side of his head. The knuckle popped in and out again. I put a left onto his nose and got him again with the right on the ear. He lurched crazily and I dropped my shoulder and slammed him back against the wall. He propped there with his arms hanging wide, gasping for breath. I hit him hard, very low, with both hands, and he went down. He vomited and his eyes closed.

I'd been right about the gun; it was a nine-millimetre Browning Hi-Power, very popular in Europe. It carries thirteen shots in the magazine, and this one was fully loaded with one bullet in the chamber. It was the most powerful handgun I'd ever seen. It looked dangerous even lying on the floor against the wall, and I handled it with a kind of revulsion. I recovered the cord, unknotted and tied Rex Houdini-style, hands and feet. His eyes opened and he swore at me.

'Don't do that, Rex,' I said. 'I've only kicked you once; I owe you a few.'

I took a big mouthful of the water, swilled it around and spat it on the floor. It was frothy and red; he was a good puncher, Rex. I drank some water.

That left me with a gun I didn't like and not much else. It was a straight road away from the house and there was no cover for hundreds of yards on either side of it. The Land Cruiser was still parked in front of the house, but my chances of commandeering it were slim; I could hardly hot-wire a Holden, let alone a Land Cruiser, and there might be more ugly people in the house or around the estate. I stood in the shadowed part of the doorway and thought that what I really needed was a Honda 750 or a telephone, or both.

As I watched, an old Japanese car drove up the road. Its rust spots jarred with the pristine white railing and superphosphated fields. The car made the turn at the top of the drive and came to a stop, pointing back towards the road and about fifty yards from the squash court. A man in a checked jacket and dark trousers got out, reached back into the car for what looked like a bundle of papers, and walked up towards the house. He was gangling and young with longish, untidy fair hair. He didn't look like one of Mr Big's minions or like the next-door neighbour calling in for coffee. His trouser bottoms flapped as he walked and the hem of his jacket was down at the back.

He went up the steps and knocked on the front door. After a minute or so, a man I hadn't seen before opened the door. The untidy man started talking and the other guy began shaking his head. I bent as low as I could, given that my ribs were starting to hurt insistently, and scooted across to the car. I opened the back door, rolled in and pulled the door shut. There was nothing to hide under. I just scrunched myself down on the floor and hoped.

The door opened, there was a slap as something hit the back seat, the door slammed, the springs creaked and the car started. I stayed down for twice as long as I thought I needed to and when I risked a peep we were clear of the property. I looked at the driver, but you can't do much in the way of character assessment from the back of a head. He had dandruff. I sat upright behind him and tapped him on the shoulder. He started and swung the wheel.

'Don't worry,' I said. 'Steer straight.'

'Who're you? What do you want?' His voice cracked and broke with alarm.

'I've had a bit of trouble back there. You got me clear of it. I want to go to the railway, that's all.'

'The police, more likely.'

I brought up the Browning and showed it to him. 'I didn't

want to do this, but it has to be the railway. I don't want to hurt you.'

'Are you a prisoner?'

I laughed but the sound came our harsh and humourless. 'No; it's too complicated to explain. Do you know whose house that is back there?'

'No.'

'What the hell were you doing there?'

'Canvassing. I'm the Labor candidate for the state election.'

'Jesus. What did he say to you?'

'Told me to piss off.' The conversation seemed to give him some confidence. 'Uh, Bill Anderson's my name. What's yours?'

'Good name,' I said, 'top of the ballot. I've voted Labor all my life, when I've voted. Gough Whitlam's the greatest Australian this century.'

'That's right.'

I was going to ask him where the hell we were, but I thought it might scare him. People who don't know where they are sometimes don't know other things, like that they shouldn't kill people. The country was familiar anyway, flat, with the hills in the distance, well-watered. The side road hit the highway and I knew where I was—Camden, Macarthur Onslow country, wool country, fat lambs and fat cheques. I hadn't told him my name and he hadn't said he was going to take me to the railway station, but we were still moving and still talking.

'What hope do you have around here, Bill?'

'Not much. Safe Country Party, but you never know.' He turned onto the highway.

'Is this the way to the railway station?'

'Yes. I don't know why, but I suppose I'll take you. I don't really think you'd use the gun.'

'You're right, I wouldn't. I've got an aunt in Camden; I'll tell her to vote for you. Hell, I'll get her to man the booth.'

He laughed. 'Well, I'll need everyone I can get. Can you tell me what sort of trouble you're in?'

'No, it's Sydney trouble. I'm going back to sort it out.'

'With the gun?'

'No.' I dropped the gun onto the front seat beside him. 'Where's the station?'

'Bout a mile. Got any money?'

I'd felt the tightly folded money dig into me several times during the ordeal. It was still there.

'A bit. Trains regular?'

'No. Look, I'll drive you into town.'

I was surprised, and moved to the side to get a better look at him. He was thirtyish and the fair hair fell forward onto his forehead and hung down over his ears. He had a beaky nose and a strong chin. He needed a shave.

'I'll buy the petrol, then,' I said. 'You can stop anywhere. Nobody's looking for me yet.'

We crossed the Nepean River and Anderson stopped at a BP station. A liquor store across the road beckoned and I went across and bought a six-pack. I paid for the petrol, got in the front seat and offered Anderson a beer. He shook his head.

'Never touch it before five. Can't in my game.'

'Which is what?'

'School teaching.' He started the car and we headed for Sydney. 'It's amazing, you know. That gun was on the front seat the whole time we were there getting the petrol. The garage bloke didn't see it, or if he saw it he didn't care.'

'It's television,' I said. 'We're learning to love the gun.'

'Is it yours?'

'Hell, no. I took it off a heavy back at Sunnybrook Farm.'

He grunted and concentrated on driving. The car was a Datsun with a lot of miles on the clock; it bounced around and I had the feeling that Anderson was nursing it. I sucked on a can, conscious of the delicious cold sting of the beer on my cut mouth. I put the gun on the floor and looked out of the streaky window. The Camden district is littered with sandstone buildings drenched in convict sweat. It's all worth a look on a relaxed drive, but I wasn't relaxed.

'Are you just being the original good bloke, or are you helping me for a reason?' I opened the second can and put the empty one carefully down beside the Browning.

'Bit of both,' he said. 'I'm curious about that house.'

'Why?'

'There's a mystery about it. No-one seems to know who owns it. It changed hands a while back. Do you know who owns it?'

'No.'

'Another thing. I've been told that some pretty high-up people in the opposition have been spending some time out there recently. I thought I'd call in and have a look. Do you know anything about that, a political angle?'

'No. It shouldn't be hard to trace the owner, though—registers and such.'

'I did that. It's a company. I forget the name, but I tried to trace it and got another company.'

'Ah, ha. Like that.'

'Yes, and now you pop up all beaten up and carrying a gun. Pretty interesting.'

'Yeah. Tell you what, I'll be looking into all this in Sydney. Anything useful I turn up I'll put you onto. Okay?'

'Take one of the leaflets.'

I reached back and got one. It advised voters to go for Anderson first up and featured a picture of him with his hair trimmed and wearing a tie and a smile.

'Office number's on the back.'

I put the paper in my pocket and finished the can. My head hurt where it had hit the pavement; my wrists hurt where they'd been roped; my shoulder ached and my ribs throbbed. I was in great shape.

The traffic wasn't too bad at that time of day and we moved along smartly towards the metropolis. When I asked him to stop, he looked across the road, surprised.

'The university?'

'Yeah. I'm a professor of philosophy.'

He laughed. 'Hope to hear from you.'

I wished him luck in the election and he drove away. That left me tramping down Glebe Point Road towards home. The Browning inside my shirt was a bit avant-garde, but the four cans in their plastic collars were just the thing for the neighbourhood.

Hilde was at home and she went straight into action when she saw me. She ran a bath and got busy with the cotton wool, antiseptic and adhesive tape.

'Very nasty,' she said, looking at the shoulder and the ribs. 'Open your mouth.'

I did and swore because it hurt.

'Lucky you didn't lose some teeth.'

I nodded. I've lost a few over the years and can't spare any more. It seemed I'd put a few teeth into my tongue and that one of Rex's punches had split the skin inside the mouth and pulped up one section of gum a bit. I wouldn't be chewing on any steaks for a while. While Hilde dabbed at me, I thought of a few of my friends who'd fought professionally in the late 1950s. I could remember the girlfriend of one of them saying that she was the greatest soup maker in Sydney because that's all her bloke could eat most of the time. I'd walked into a moving piece of two by four in one of my early jobs and Cyn had cried when she saw me. I tried to push the memories away.

'The ribs worry me,' Hilde said. She touched a raw rip in the skin, surrounded by a bluish bruise. 'How did that happen?'

'At a disco. I fell and they danced on me.'

She snorted and pressed some tape into place, not gently. I put the beer in the fridge, resisted the wine and made a pot of coffee. Hilde went off to Tooth Capping III. I phoned Ann Winter's less salubrious address and got a woman on the line with a slurred voice and uncertain grammar. She said she'd seen Ann come in the previous night and go again that morning. That was fine, but the woman sounded drunk already.

'What day is it?' I asked.

'Wednesday.'

'Right. Look, how was Ann? Was she okay?'

'She was pissed off; someone dumped her at a party or somethin'. Hey!' Her voice was suddenly clearer, as if she'd got her tongue working. 'Are you Cliff?'

'Yes.'

'Get stuffed, Cliff.' She hung up.

It sounded as if my connection to Ann Winter had got looser. That was a pity, but I was relieved that none of the rough stuff had reached her. I shaved around the cuts and abrasions, put on some clean clothes and went off to see my favourite policeman.

14

FRANK Parker looked tired. The hours he'd been working were stencilled on his face in the eye pouches and the grooves beside his mouth. His ashtray overflowed with those judiciously smoked butts.

'What happened to you?' he enquired.

I touched my swollen lip and was conscious that I was holding myself carefully on account of the ribs. I perched on the nearest desk. The detective who had ignored us before was at his desk ignoring us again.

'All in the line of work, Frank. You should get out more. Take a good belting on the street. All this paper work isn't good for you. I thought you were going to get help.'

'I got help, but so far the help just makes more work,' he growled. 'And I have been on the street. We pulled up a kid in a hot car last night. Took eight minutes—the paper work's taking eight hours.'

'Nothing on the Henneberry case?'

'No. You?'

'Hard to say. I got picked up last night by some hired hands. We went on a drive into the country.'

He groaned. 'You're not here to lay charges of assault and abduction?'

'No. I got out of it with a split lip and a bent rib. They were heavy boys, though. Take a look at this.' The security is lousy at that place. I'd walked through it with a fourteen shot Browning Hi-Power in my jacket pocket. I put the gun on Frank's desk on top of a pile of carbon copies of something. He pushed it around with the tip of a pencil so that the muzzle was pointing towards his colleague.

'You went up against this, Hardy?'

'More around it. I met the boss. I wonder if you can tell me who he is.'

He lit a cigarette and looked interested. 'Try me.'

'His place is out Camden way, pretty nice layout. His boys are named Rex, he's a snappy dresser with a good hook, and . . .' I felt for the name, 'Tal. He's a Yank who did the driving. Rex had the Browning there, Tal had some little thing. The boss's about sixty, tall and thin, looks a bit sick. He's got what the Americans call a cocksucker moustache.'

Frank blew smoke. 'Oh, yeah? Why do they call it that?'

'I don't know.' I fingered my upper lip. 'Small, wouldn't get in the way?'

Frank's expression of disgust gave him rock-solid heterosexual credentials.

'Freddy Ward,' he said.

'Who's he?'

'One of the boys. He and Singer and Tom McLeary divided up the action in the eastern suburbs. He's done some rough things in his time, but I thought he was taking it easy.'

'He certainly looked sick. I got the feeling that he was a bit past it. But he's got a foul temper and bugger all control. He didn't leave the rough stuff to his boys. I just gave him a bit of cheek and you should've seen him.'

'That's him. I hear that Freddy might not be the full dollar. He was in Changi, which wouldn't have done him any good. What did he want with you?'

'He wanted to know who I was working for.'

'Did you tell him?'

'No. They said they'd drop me in a hole if I didn't, but I had the feeling they'd do it if I did.'

A woman sailed past and dropped a folder on his desk. Parker swore and dragged hard on his cigarette. 'You think this is all connected with the Henneberry thing? There's a bit of heat in that, by the way.'

'I don't know. What sort of heat?'

'His father's a senator or something. I had some fucking Foreign Affairs bloke on the phone, wanting results.'

'Have you checked Henneberry out with the spooks?'

'Yeah.' He hunted in the OUT tray and pulled up a file. I reached for it, but he snapped it away and grinned. 'They say,' he ran his finger down a page and quoted, '. . . that he had no connection with any security services'.

'Do you believe them?'

He shrugged. 'Who knows? Lying's their business. D'you see Rex and his mate fixing Henneberry?'

'No.'

'What's next, then?'

'Get out and ask questions.'

'Ask who?'

I stood up. 'Brother Gentle.'

He looked blankly at me. I gave him a wave and left him with his papers and Rex's big gun.

It seemed like time to check in with my client but, given all the interest around town in who that was, it also seemed like time to play it cagey. If I'd gone to my office I could have put my feet on the desk, breathed the air of inspiration and been at my very best on the line, but I might also have had listeners-in. I rang Mrs Marion Singer from a public phone and instructed her to go out and ring the booth I was in. I waited ten minutes, faking a call and infuriating two would-be users.

'Was that necessary?' she asked.

'Maybe. Do you know a man named Ward?'

'Fred Ward? I know *of* him. What about him?'

'He gave me a little trouble. Look, Mrs Singer, this is all getting very complicated.' I told her about Henneberry and Leon and my trip to Camden.

'I'm sorry for all that,' she said, without sounding sorry. 'But what about John?'

'I'm still on it.'

'Stay on it.' she hung up. No more offers of money, no more information.

The bright, dry spell we'd had in Sydney for a week or more looked like coming to an end. There was a coolness in the air and the wind was lifting; it was an indecisive wind, picking up things, tossing them about and putting them down. The clouds that had been light and high for days were darkening and coming down. I caught a cab to Bronte, keeping my fingers crossed that my car would still be there. It was. The radio aerial had been snapped off and 'Screw Fraser' had been scratched on the bonnet.

The rain started as I drove to the ashram. It beat down while I sat in the car and looked the place over. The posters were artfully made and they seemed to shine out through the curtain of rain. I subscribe to the belief that rain accentuates aches and pains. I had plenty to be accentuated; if well-being is a lack of consciousness about the body, I wasn't well. If I moved my head sharply, my brain broke its moorings for an instant, and when I accidentally elbowed myself in the side I felt as if a jagged rib bone was going to pierce a lung. 'GIVE' was glowing through the rain but I felt more like taking. A holiday, for example. I could go to Lew Hoad's tennis ranch in Spain. I've always wanted to see it. Good old Glebe boy, Lew. I could work up a topspin backhand and try to beat Hilde. Lew and I could have a few beers and talk about Pancho Gonzales and Pancho Segura. I saw Segura and Rosewall once—the cunningest tennis match ever played.

It was a nice thought, but now I had people scurrying into a yellow building with yellow pants legs and sandals showing under yellow slickers. There's nothing like a little damp to force mendicants inside off the street. I found a raincoat in the back of the car and squirmed into it, hurting my side again. It helped to hide the bulge of the gun I stuck in my belt.

I ran for the door, pushed it open and dripped water on the yellow carpet. The reception nook was empty but I noticed the business end of a TV camera high on a wall. Wired for sight, wired for sound.

'Peace,' I said to the camera. 'Cliff Hardy here. Is Brother Gentle available?'

After two minutes a man came through the door, looking both brotherly and gentle. He was short and plump with thin brown hair brushed carefully across his rounded skull. He had a receding chin and meek eyes. I said my name and put my hand out. He took my hand in both of his and pressed. It felt like warm dough kneading back.

'What can I do for you, Mr Hardy?' He had a lisp, too. It was almost too much gentleness to take in one day.

'I'm a private investigator,' I said. 'Here's my licence.' I showed him the paper and he shook his head slowly.

'I'm sorry for you,' he said.

'How's that?'

'Identification papers, licences and you carry a gun. You must be very afraid.'

'Not all the time. Is there somewhere we can talk?'

'Of course.' His sandals creaked and slapped as he walked back through the door. His stiff yellow jacket and limp yellow trousers rustled as he moved. He opened a door with a thin, blue-veined hand that carried several rings on several fingers.

We went into a larger room with the same decor; it was like stepping into the middle of an apricot. The windows were blanked out, there was carpet on the floor and some thin mats on top of the carpet in the middle of the room. A life-sized, that is, about five foot tall, statue of the Himmler look-alike stood in the corner. It was gilded like the girl in *Goldfinger*.

Brother Gentle squatted on one of the mats and motioned me to do the same. I'm a cultural experimenter. I squatted.

'I can't imagine how I can help you, Mr Hardy. Our worlds are far apart.'

'They're connected, though. I want you to tell me all you know about a man named Leon.'

He looked blank and I hoped he wasn't going into a trance.

'A derelict who came here recently.' I realised suddenly that I had no idea what Leon had looked like. 'A drunk,' I improvised, 'middle-aged and looking older. A deadbeat.'

'Indeed,' he said. 'A lost one, truly lost. Leon Bronowski.'

'I didn't know his other name.'

'Few would, I suppose. Fewer still would care.'

I felt the reproach and defended myself. 'I never met him.' As soon as I had said it, I was aware that he'd won a little strategic battle. I tried to recover the ground. 'Did you know him well?'

'I met him once. He sat just where you are sitting. He was drunk and he wanted money. He's a Russian and he speaks six languages.' He did a little more headshaking. 'Six languages and no enlightenment. Very sad.'

'What did you talk about?'

'Money. He was a very unhappy man. Still is, I imagine.'

'He's dead.' I wondered if he'd put his palms together or touch his forehead to the floor, but instead he let go one of his full-on gentle smiles.

'Then he is unhappy no longer.'

'That's one way of looking at it. Did he just come straight out and ask for money, or what? He must have had some line.' The squatting position was uncomfortable for my battered ribs and I winced as I spoke. He looked at me curiously.

'You positively radiate pressure, tension and disharmony, Mr Hardy.'

'Possibly. You can pick that up, eh?'

'Yes, indeed.'

'The split lip probably helps. I'll admit it was smart of you to spot the gun. What about Leon?'

'He tried to bargain with me.' Now he did put his palms together. He rubbed them as if he liked the feeling, or maybe he liked bargains.

'What did he have to bargain with?'

The rubbing went on with a surprisingly dry sound, considering how moist his hands had felt. 'He seemed to think that I preyed on people, particularly old people. The Movement cares for a number of old people, of course.'

'Naturally, but I don't see what you're getting at.'

'He told me about a place where I could get recruits—victims, I think he called them. He was very agitated about it.'

'You said he was drunk?'

'He was drunk when he started, or so I thought. I don't have a lot of experience of the condition. But he seemed to want to talk about this place, although he must have seen that I was not able to give him money. He was calmer after I had talked to him. How did he die?'

'He was murdered,' I said, roughly. 'What was this place he talked about? D'you remember?'

'Of course.' He looked surprised at the suggestion that people forgot things. 'A house in Monk Lane, Clovelly. Number ten. I gathered there were a lot of old people there, damaged people like himself.'

'Have you checked the place? Send anyone out?'

He stopped the rubbing and opened his hands up in a gesture of innocence. 'He was mistaken Mr Hardy. I do not recruit people. They come to me, to the Movement, that is.'

I nodded. A house full of damaged old people that had shaken Leon Bronowski up. He'd mentioned it to Bruce Henneberry, maybe in response to a question about Singer. It felt solid, more than the fantasy of a booze-clouded brain, and there were two dead men, two men removed from the possibility of unhappiness, to give it solidity.

I reached back for my money. 'Do you accept donations?' I couldn't call him anything. The embarrassment I felt at the thought of calling him 'Brother' or 'Brother Gentle' reminded me of the years I'd spent not calling my wife's father anything. Come to think of it, this guy looked a bit like him—Cyn had got her looks from her mother. He inclined his head graciously and I put twenty bucks on the floor between us. I was suddenly aware of how quiet it was. The silence was like the reverse side of a shriek.

'Why is it so quiet?' I asked.

'One of our principles,' he said. 'We believe that excessive noise disturbs the harmonies of mind, body and soul. There is a vow of silence in operation here and we try to do everything quietly.'

He was certainly doing well at that. As I put my money away, I touched the pictures of Singer. *What the hell*, I thought, I pulled them out and showed them to him, asking him if he'd ever seen the subject.

He didn't hesitate. 'Never. An interesting face.'

'You read faces?'

'You are a cynic, Mr Hardy. Yes I can read faces. I could tell you a great deal about yourself from yours.'

I rubbed my hand over what he was talking about. 'Not so hard,' I said. 'Broken nose—boxing; missing teeth—enemies; lines and wrinkles—I used to smoke a lot.'

'There's a lot more, but you wouldn't listen.' He handed the pictures back. 'This man is highly intelligent. He is capable of great violence, perhaps to himself.'

'Thanks.' I could always serve that up to Mrs Singer and explain that a man dressed like a canary had told me so. 'What's the significance of the yellow?' I asked.

'You would have to join us to find that out, Mr Hardy.'

I stood up. I hadn't seen him move, but the twenty dollars had gone away somewhere very quietly. He conducted me back to the reception room and pressed my hand again.

'I hope you don't have to use the gun, Mr Hardy. Guns make a lot of noise.'

'So they do,' I said. 'And blood is red.'

'You are a poet. I will repeat that to our spiritual leader when he visits us next year.'

The comment had the soft phoniness peculiar to the religious conman. On the whole, I prefer the spiel of the oil share sellers and real estate crooks.

'Feel free,' I said.

15

IT was late in the afternoon and the rain had eased to a drizzle that looked like settling in for the night. I gave the street a careful once over before going across to my car. Freddy Ward didn't seem like the sort of man to call it all square, and I wouldn't have been surprised if Rex decided to go freelance for a night. I deeply suspected Rex of being vindictive. But I couldn't see any watchers and cruisers and they stand out plainly in the rain when honest folk are inside or going about their business fast.

My *Gregorys* showed Monk Lane to be a little trickle of a thoroughfare in Clovelly near the boundary with Randwick. Leon had had a long beat. I drove down to the beach and sat and sorted out my thoughts on the matter or matters before me. It was smoking time again, moody time with the light rain rinsing the air and turning the sand grey. My first impulse was to front up to the house and compare my photographs with the faces of all the old jokers there. Against that were Henneberry's guts on the carpet and all Leon's broken bones. Maybe I needed reinforcements. More than that, I needed information; walking up to that house to knock on the front door could be like walking up to the Lubianka. The only person I could think of with the kind of street knowledge I needed was Ann Winter. A flock of seagulls landed on the sand and began to walk down towards the water as if they knew what they were doing. I started the car and drove to Manny's.

There was a sprinkle of people in the coffee bar but no sign of the proprietor. A thin blonde was doing the honours in a lackadaisical way, as if her body was somewhere else as well as her mind. I bought a coffee and asked if Ann had been in recently.

'Yeah, she was. Said she'd be back later.'

'When?'

She shrugged.

'Mind if I use the tape machine?'

She shrugged again.

I picked out a blank tape, slipped it into the slot and recited: 'Ann, Cliff Hardy. I'm sorry about the other night. I didn't dump you. I ran into some trouble, very heavy stuff. Now I'm going to number ten Monk Lane, Clovelly. Looks like the lead Bruce and Leon had. I'm going for a look-see but maybe you know something about the place. I'll wait outside for an hour. It's six-fifteen now. If you hear this before seven-thirty come on over. I'll pay for the cab. Thought you'd want to see this through'. I wrote 'For Ann Winter' on the cassette label and asked the girl to give it to Ann if she came in.

'You haven't drunk your coffee,' she said.

I swilled it down, wishing it had a touch of Manny's grappa in it and went back out into the rain. The roads were greasy and treacherous as I wound up through the cutting to Clovelly. It was steep going and I wondered how many times Leon had hoofed it in all the years he'd bummed around this district. With some derelicts, the walking is what keeps them alive. It strikes a balance with the sugar and alcohol in their systems and they stay thin and hard like a tree that's rotting inside but still standing. Eventually the rot wins.

Clovelly is a headland tucked in south of Bronte and east of Randwick. It's a bit like those two suburbs, but down market on both of them. The flats are a bit meaner, the house fronts and the streets narrower. Monk Lane was thin, twisted and a dead end. It held a mixture of faded, tired-looking flats and houses. Number ten was at the end of the street with a vacant block on one side and a crumbling, roofless cottage on the other. A sheer rock wall with some creeper clinging to it rose up behind the house, which was three storeys high, heavy and ungracious. It had the unmistakable look of a building divided into flats and single rooms.

It was a forbidding pile. There was a narrow cement walkway

94

down one side and it was a fair bet that the skimpy backyard would be a jungle of privet and castor oil trees. It differed from most other places in that the backyard had privacy; around here the terrain is such that every block is fully visible from some higher elevation. Not here, but there was a good chance of getting rubbish thrown down into the back from the top of the rock.

I sat in the car and looked at it, giving Ann time to show up. She didn't. I had no good ideas on how to tackle the place, so I got my gun out again and stuck it in my belt. That sometimes helps, as I get to thinking of ways to avoid having to use it, but this time nothing helpful came. I hunted out the most anonymous card in my collection, which read, 'BRIAN HARRISON—INDEPENDENT SYSTEMS'. It had been left under my door and I never found out who Brian was or what an independent system might be. I put the card in my pocket and stuck my hand out of the window. The rain had stopped; no excuses. There was no activity in the street. One of the lights had blown and it was dark so I took a torch with me.

I walked down the side of the building, scouting. There were a couple of broken windows boarded up at the back where the outside plumbing rusted and dripped. I skidded on some rubbish on the path and crashed into a couple of battered garbage bins. One went over and spilled a cascade of pet food tins that bounced and rattled over the concrete to meet a pile of flagons, some broken.

I scooted back up the path to the building's entrance, which was a sort of porch with a low rail stuck to the side like an afterthought. There were buttons numbered one to ten beside the door; I pushed number one and heard it ring inside, close by. While I waited, I pressed a few other buttons and heard nothing.

The door in front of me opened inwards, and from long habit I moved forward and put my foot up on the step.

'Yes?' He looked as if he got more practice at saying no, although not necessarily in English. He was small and dark with a sallow, pocked complexion and a mouth that turned down sourly. His forehead was high and deeply creased with frown marks. He wore dirty boots, jeans and a loose sports shirt outside the jeans. I'd have put his age at around thirty. His forearms were sinewy with dark, downy hair; his biceps looked as if they would bunch up like cricket balls. He pulled a grubby handkerchief from a back pocket and wiped his nose.

'Er, Mr . . .?' He didn't say anything and I had to take the plunge. I handed him the card. 'I have to check the foundations—main roads and council job. They'll be working in the area soon, blasting and tunnelling, so we need to know how sound the buildings in the area are.' I took two steps back and glanced around. 'Looks okay, but I've got to check.'

He came forward and put the card on the railing. I couldn't tell whether he'd read it or not, or whether he could read it.

'Very late,' he said. The voice was light, almost singsong. There was an accent, not Greek, but like it.

'I'm sorry, but I must look.'

'Inside or outside?'

'Oh, outside, mostly, have to look at any basements or cellars. Just that, unless there's any major cracks.' I'd already noticed a big crack that ran raggedly up at the back.

'Council?'

'And the Department of Main Roads.' I tried to give the words all the weight I could, and thought some jargon might help. 'There's the flight path to consider, too. Decibels. I won't be long, it's miserable out.'

He tapped the breast pocket of his shirt. Keys clinked and there seemed to be some muscular development up there too. He pulled the door closed behind him.

'I will take you.'

We walked along the path to the back and I bent down to flash the torch at the foundations from time to time. Some of the bricks were crumbling.

'Damp course trouble?'

He shrugged. At the back he pulled out his keys and we went down a set of steps that the vines and weeds were threatening. He unlocked the padlock on a heavy door; it swung in and he flicked on the light. It was a small, airless cave, dark despite the bulb. There was another door a few feet into the shadows. It had a strange smell, but how are old cellars supposed to smell? I took a perfunctory look around, said 'Okay', and went up the steps. He locked the door and I pointed to the crack running up the bricks. It had fractured a heavy window ledge on the second floor and looked as if it might run up behind a drainpipe to the roof.

'I'll have to check that,' I said. 'Inside, sorry.'

He looked dubious but I bustled back along the path. 'Got two other places to see tonight,' I said. 'Let's get this over with.'

He unlocked the front door and we went into a small lobby with a door on the left and a staircase on the right.

'You go up,' he said.

The passage looked as if it hadn't been swept that year or last. The carpet strip was ragged and there was a coating of dust on the dry, flaky boards on either side of it. There were several doors down one side. It was hard to tell in the gloom, but I thought I saw fittings for outside locking. He padded softly along behind me, the keys clinking in his pocket.

At the end of the passage he quickened his pace, stepped in front of me and unlocked the door.

'No-one in here,' he said.

But someone had been in there and pretty recently. The room had two distinct smells—old, stale alcohol and the one that comes from handwashed socks and underwear.

It was completely dark outside now. He turned on the light and blew his nose at the same time. The bulb was fly-spotted, like most of the surfaces in the room. On the floor was the inevitable lino, worn through to the newspaper strata in some places and through to the boards in others. Although the night was mild, the room was cold. Plaster had fallen off the wall in lumps above the skirting board and the stuff that hung on glistened wetly. There was some junky furniture, wood-veneered and peeling. The bed was narrow and the mattress was an ancient, sweat-stained ruin. Cobwebs hung in the corners like thick skeins of grey wool.

I heard movements above me, footsteps and something being dropped. The thought of someone living in conditions like these sickened me. I tensed up, my ribs hurt and I moved angrily across to examine the broken window ledge and to give myself a moment to think. It didn't take much thinking—the place was a gaol of some kind and I had the turnkey right there with me. It looked just like the sort of place that a damaged or deranged person such as Singer had been reported to be could end up in. I took the .45 from my belt, cocked it and turned. I pointed the gun at his nose.

'I'm searching this dump from top to bottom. You're opening the doors.'

He was incredibly quick. One minute his eyes were registering surprise and the next he was in a crouch and scuttling forward to swing a stiff arm at me like a scythe. He wasn't balanced quite right, though, and the light wasn't good for that sort of action. The arm missed and I slammed the side of his head with the butt of the automatic. It got him just above the temple and he grunted and went down. I put the muzzle hard in his ear and felt in his shirt pocket for the keys. I hooked a finger round them but then I felt the soft, loose movement under my hand and pulled away as if I'd touched a snake. The contours of the chest weren't muscular. With my well-placed gun butt, I'd just floored a woman.

It was obvious now; the short, dark hair curling around the ears was softer than a man's hair, and with the shirt pushed up I could see the roundness of her hips. It didn't mean that she wasn't a nasty, dangerous bit of work. I kept the gun pressed close while she shook her head and hurt herself.

'You're not a lady,' I said. 'Get on the bed.' She didn't move. With an amateur I'd have delivered a boot to the bum for emphasis, but she was no amateur. Her eyes were shining with anticipation of more fighting. My side was hurting and I'd done something to the knuckle that had popped when I'd hit Rex. I wouldn't have backed myself in a fair return fight. A swinging foot would give her all the chance she'd need. I stepped back and pointed the gun at her knee.

'Get on the bed or I'll cripple you.'

She said something unpleasant-sounding in a language I didn't understand and got on the bed.

'Turn to the wall.'

She turned and I checked the window. It was nailed shut. If she kicked it in she'd have a twenty-five-foot drop in the dark onto the garbage bins, the cans and the broken bottles. I wouldn't have risked it.

'Take off your shoes, easy.'

She bent her legs up, unzipped the boots and kicked them off onto the floor. I slung them into the passage, smashed the light bulb with the gun barrel and went through the door in three strides. I pinned the door closed with my shoulder and ran around the key ring until I found the one that locked it. It seemed unlikely that she'd have a spare key, but I waited outside for a while to be sure. I heard the bed creak and scratching noises as she felt her way around and that was all.

Going through that house was one of the most depressing things I've ever done. I did it methodically, starting at the top back and working through to bottom front. There were thirteen single rooms and five flatettes with twenty-three occupants. Without exception they were middle-aged or older, and defeated. The ones doubling up in the flatettes were the worst off. A few of them got abusive when I barged in, youngish, healthy and carrying a gun. One old man made a pathetic attempt to take me and I had to gentle him back into a chair.

The squalor of the rooms was profound. They smelled, were dirt-encrusted and there were signs of the depredations of vermin everywhere. The people were living on bread, pet food and cheap wine. There were three toilets in the building, cracked, creaking affairs that flushed about a pint of water. I looked at one chamber pot in one room. Only one.

Most of the occupants wore pyjamas or nightgowns and dressing-gowns. I had to look closely at some of the sunken-in, hopeless faces to determine their sex. They were so far gone it didn't matter, but some of those who looked like women wore pyjamas and some of those who looked like men wore nightgowns, pathetic nylon affairs with filthy, phony lace.

I forced myself to do the whole round. In one single room a woman tottered towards me, holding out a photograph. I took the picture, which was of a young woman wearing a bathing suit and high heels in a cheesecake pose.

'Is this you?' I said.

She cackled at me. She was skeletally thin and she scratched at her groin with fleshless, bony hands. When she stopped scratching there, she moved the hand up to her head. I stepped back.

'What's your name?'

Scratch, scratch. Hair and flakes of skin fell onto her shoulders. 'I don't know,' she said hoarsely. 'What's yours, dear?'

There were no radios in the rooms, a few magazines, no books. I only glanced into a few drawers and cupboards but there were no pens or pencils. Spoons, bowls and cups were made of plastic.

The smell was bad everywhere, but in one room I nearly vomited from the stench. The floor was a sea of cockroaches and a man was sitting on the bed watching them with a rapt, engrossed smile on his face.

I locked all the occupants in as they were, because I couldn't think of anything else to do. They mumbled at me and each other in slow, toneless voices that were curiously alike. They dribbled and spat. None of them was John Singer.

16

THE only habitable part of the place was the flatette in front where the turnkey lived. The four rooms were only moderately clean but their toilet and bathroom, small kitchen and functioning furniture put them in the luxury department. There was food for humans in the cupboards and refrigerator and a decent flagon of red wine on the kitchen table. I rinsed a glass, filled it with wine, drank it down and poured again. I thought very seriously about the packet of cigarettes on the table beside the flagon, but decided on more wine instead. I drank more of it than I wanted to and was feeling the effect pretty soon. I was drinking to get the stink and taste of those foul rooms out of my head.

Then I searched the flatette and I didn't care what got disturbed or broken. I felt bad when I started—bad from the beating I'd taken the day before and because of the prisoners' empty eyes and from the wine—and I felt worse as I worked. The woman I'd locked up in room twelve was one Mary Mahoud, thirty four, a naturalised Australian. Ms Mahoud had been doing a highly illegal stunt, one that would earn her about twenty years' worth of imprisonment. The records were thorough and well-kept: the occupants of number ten Monk Lane were all recipients of pensions of one sort or another. They were registered at a few different addresses and their cheques arrived and were cashed regularly, but not by them. She had something like two thousand bucks coming in weekly. From what I'd seen, the overheads were low.

I found the explanation for the sameness of the prisoners' apathetic and listless behaviour—a cupboard full of Valium, Mogadon and other preparations. There was also a big stock of laxatives, sleeping pills and painkillers. A bottom drawer in a dresser was locked and I smashed it open. There was a different set of records inside—envelopes with the surnames printed in bold, black capitals and a date. I flicked through a few: 'Jane Harman Ogilvie 23.6.79'; 'Elizabeth Hodges 1.12.80' There were about a dozen of them, and it wasn't hard to guess what they were—the dead file. The name 'Singer' didn't appear.

I didn't fancy the next part and when I went out into the lobby Mary Mahoud gave me a chance to put it off. She was drumming on the door of number twelve and sobbing to be let out. The door was holding strong.

'Shut up!' I gave the door a thump with the gun.

'Out, out, out!' She chanted the word like a street demonstrator. Then she started to scream it and a racket started behind a door further down the passage. I went down and rapped on it.

'Be quiet. You want to get out of this, don't you?'

No reply.

'I've got this Mahoud bitch locked up. You'll be out tonight. Just be patient.'

The voice from behind the door was slow and querulous. I couldn't recall much about its owner; all the occupants had blended in my mind into one geriatric mass. 'Locked up? Mary?'

'Right. It's over. She's going to gaol.'

A low, ragged chuckle began, growing into a piercing, near-hysterical laugh. Mahoud must have heard it because she went quiet for a minute and then started sobbing again and hitting the door. I went back and spoke harshly with my mouth close to the wood.

'You heard that, didn't you? If you don't shut up, I'll come in there and knock you out, then I'll put you in a room with nine or ten of them and watch what happens. How'd you like that?'

'No, no. Out. Anything . . . there's money.'

'Forget it and keep quiet.'

There was an interesting assortment of gear in one of Mahoud's drawers—a studded belt, a pair of handcuffs, a heavy sheath knife and a key on a ring. I took the key and went to

102

the back of the building. The key opened the inner chamber to the cellar. It was the cleanest room I'd found so far. The concrete was swept and the whitewashed walls gleamed under the hard fluorescent light. In one corner was an instrument that reminded me of my mother's washing copper. It was a large metal tub, with a close-fitting lid. It was gas heated and mounted under a tap. Beside it was a shelf carrying a five-kilo bag of lime and a bigger bag of cement. I lifted the lid. The tub was scummy and smelt bad. There was also a scummy, foul-smelling bucket behind it. I went back to the outer chamber and used my torch to look in the corners where the light didn't shine. There was a set of gardening tools leaning higgledy-piggledy against the wall and a heavy straight digging bar lay on the floor in front of them.

The claret I'd drunk wasn't giving me courage, but it was stimulating my thinking. The name 'Singer' didn't appear on the house records, but I remembered what Ann had said about the changeability of names on this social level and the dodges used to beat the social security computer. The wine was also stimulating my imagination: under the severe light I could see the tub bubbling and the lime-laced water breaking down tissue. Bones broke and pulverised easily, most of them. The gardening tools were clean and the lush growth in the backyard was an obscenity.

I'd decided it was time to call the cops when I heard the scrape of footsteps outside. I hit the light switch and moved into the outer section of the cellar. I bumped the door going through and the key jumped out and skidded across the floor. Then there was a flurried movement and a dark shape stumbled down towards me into the cellar. I reached for the gun in my belt but a torch beam hit me in the eyes.

'Touch the gun and I'll kill you, Hardy.' I shaded my eyes and saw Manny standing up in the doorway looking wide and solid. He was holding the pump-action shotgun the way a carpenter holds a saw, familiarly and with affection. I had no hope of getting my gun out, and, besides, hanging onto my arm, cursing and breathing hard, was Ann Winter.

Manny lifted the gun a fraction. 'The key is by your left foot, Hardy. Kick it over.'

I did. He moved smoothly, the way he did in his coffee bar, and scooped them up.

'Now, put the gun on the ground and slide it across. Softly, please.' He was enjoying himself. I did that, too, and he put it in his pocket with the key. This meant that he had only one hand on the shotgun for an instant, but he had it tucked back safe and steady. He'd learned to do all this in some very good school.

'Where's Mary?'

I didn't answer. Ann moved even closer to me, which was convenient for him if he was going to shoot. Down there the gun would make a lot of noise. I reckoned he'd fire if he had to, but not just because I wouldn't tell him where Mary was. He came down the steps and backed us up with the shotgun until we were against the wall. Still watching us, he swung aside to open the inner cellar door. A wave of the gun did all the talking necessary. We went in and he locked the door.

I turned the fluorescent tube on again. Ann's face was stark white and her lips were twitching.

'I don't understand this,' she said shakily.

'The other night,' I said. 'After the wake. What happened to you?'

'Nothing. They didn't touch me. Screw that, what's happening *here*?'

I didn't answer. I was trying to think whether I'd seen any indications in the records that more than one person was involved in running the house. I hadn't, unless it was the capitals on the dead file; the rest of the writing was in a sloping longhand. But that didn't mean anything. Then it came to me and I found the reasons to reproach myself that I'd been seeking. Some of the items in the flatette—socks, a belt, a sports coat—were clearly masculine. I'd been confused by my earlier mistake about Mahoud's sex and had become careless. There was another thing—the dregs in the plastic cups had smelled like Manny's homemade vino. I should have picked up on that.

Ann pulled at my arm. 'Bugger you, Hardy. What *is* all this?'

'Manny must have killed Bruce.' I was talking mostly to myself. 'And Leon. Jesus. Leon stumbled onto this place and told Bruce about it and Manny heard the tape. Then I mentioned it on tape.' I looked at Ann. 'I left a tape for you. Did Manny hear it?'

'Yes. I played it. He said he'd give me a lift. He had the shotgun. I'm scared.' She looked around the room, at the boiling tub and the lime. 'What goes on here?'

I told her, keeping it as ungrisly as I could.

'Who's Mary?' she asked.

'Woman who runs this joint. Hard. I had to knock her about a bit.'

'He said on the way over that he'd kill you if you'd hurt her.'

'He'll kill me, anyway. He has to.'

'Oh, God.' She wasn't dumb. She could see it was one out, all out. She gripped my arm so hard that I could feel the bite of her fingers through the jacket and shirt.

'Easy,' I said. 'He won't do it here, not with the shotgun. That gives us a small chance.'

'You're crazy! What chance? He's killed two men. God, this is a nightmare.'

'Just be quiet and let me think.' I prowled around the room, but it was comfortless. The door was solid, there were no windows and the ventilation grids were high up near the roof. It was a good cell and there was nothing to think about.

A noise outside made us both jump. I was worried about the whitewashed walls; maybe they were thick enough for Manny to risk using the pump gun just twice. The door swung in and Manny stood there with Mahoud just behind him. Her eyes were wild and there was a great, dark swelling on the side of her face.

'You hurt her,' Manny said. His face was inflamed, contorted and working, the multicultural features a reddened blur of rage.

'Give it to me,' he said to Mahoud. She hesitated, possibly recalling that I'd outstepped her pretty neatly before.

'He is fast, Manfred. Be careful.'

'I'll kill him.'

'Not here,' she said. 'It is too dangerous here!'

'All right. Give me the belt and go and get the van.'

'Listen, darling.' Her voice was low and urgent. 'They are going crazy up there. I haven't done the rounds yet. They will all need the pills.'

'I'll do it while you're getting the van.'

'It wouldn't start. It could take hours.'

'I told you always to have it ready.' The shotgun was steady; it was as if he was discussing his BHP shares. He had all the control he needed. 'We've got hours. Everything is going to be just all right. Belt.'

She handed him the metal-loaded belt and went back up the steps. 'Be careful,' she said.

He jerked the gun at Ann. 'Get in the corner. Turn your face to the wall.' I watched her do it and then felt a searing pain as he lashed me across the face. I thought of going for the gun but he was moving the whole time and I couldn't even see him. He got me again on the cheek. I stumbled and the leather came down on my neck. I went down. He was methodical about it; the belt went up and down and I got it across the shoulders and down from there. The ones that hit the ribs hurt most. When he'd finished he rolled me over with his foot. I saw then that he'd held my gun on me while he'd been whipping. He pointed the .45 at my stomach.

'Later, I'm going to shoot you with this.' A few locks of hair had come loose, but he looked pretty neat otherwise.

'How did Leon find out about this place?' I said. I was hoping he'd make a mistake, but only hoping.

He swished the belt, just missing my face. 'One of them got away for a little while and talked to him.' He clamped his mouth shut and I gathered there'd be no more talking. I'd marked him down as powerful and dangerous, but I hadn't thought he was vicious in the way that this operation was. I guessed Mahoud was the brains of it. That'd be something for the prosecution to probe, for the psychiatrists to analyse. But there wasn't going to be any prosecution. I had to clarify one thing, though.

'I didn't think you were man enough to take Henneberry,' I

said. 'I saw the knife upstairs. She did it, didn't she?'

'No,' he said flatly. 'I did it. I did it all. I'll do it to you, too, if I have to.' Then he kicked me in the knee which was bent at the time. The pain travelled through me and I shuddered and closed my eyes.

When I opened them, he was gone and Ann was sitting in the corner looking at her hands. She looked oddly vulnerable without her bag. Again, no mistakes from Manny.

'He's mad,' she said. 'He's going to kill us.'

I grunted and crawled across the floor towards her. Blood was dripping into my eyes and the knee felt as if it was hot and melting away. I pulled myself up to lean back against the wall and put my hand up to my face. There was some sort of cut below the hairline but he hadn't hit my eyes. I wiped some of the blood away and tried to straighten my knee. It wouldn't straighten and the attempt made me gasp.

'Broken?' she said.

'Feels like it. Christ, I'm sorry I dragged you into this, Ann.'

'So am I, but I was in it anyway, I suppose. Hell, I wish I had a smoke, or a joint. That'd be better.'

'Sorry.'

'Stop saying that. I'd settle for a drink. God, I didn't realise how dependent I'd got.'

I thought of the ton of drugs upstairs. Maybe they'd offer us some before they killed us. That's the modern way, but I didn't think it'd be Manny's style.

She reached over to touch my arm and got a place that didn't hurt. 'What are you thinking?'

'About drugs.'

'I thought you were Mr Clean.' She was talking fast, just staying in control, but talking is as good a way as any. 'What happened to you after the wake? I was left there with Pearl, feeling like a fool.' Her fingers went tight with fear.

'I got kidnapped. Different business.'

'Great. Twice in how long? Did you get beaten up then, too?'

'Yeah.'

'Will he really kill us? With that gun?'

I didn't answer. My thoughts were running along the same lines. *Very negative, Hardy,* I thought. *My leg hurts, I want it to hurt. While it hurts, I'm alive.*

'You didn't get in touch with the police or anything, did you?' she said. 'Leave a message?'

'No. Look he's only got one gun that I've seen. You might have a chance. You'll have to be ready to run.'

'Haven't you read any books?' Her voice cracked into something like a laugh. 'He'll tie us up.'

I nodded and winced as a shaft of pain went through me. Then some sweat ran down my neck, except that it didn't feel like sweat. Slowly and painfully I turned around to look at the wall; the bricks were wet and slimy for two feet up from the floor. My mind raced and I looked around the room. My heart started beating the way it did when a long-priced horse was leading in the straight with my money on it.

'Ann. Get up and have a look inside that bag of cement.'

She looked at me as I was mad but she let go of my arm and got up. She put her hand inside the bag and when it came out there was a beautiful, one-dollar department store trowel in it.

'You're smiling,' she said.

'I used to be a bricklayer. Give it here, Annie.'

She put the trowel into my right hand and I got a grip on it which hurt me all down my side. I dug at the mortar line and the trowel went in two inches. I dug it in again, twisted and the wet mortar fell out like icing off a cake.

I looked at Ann. She pulled her scarf from around her neck, spat on it and rubbed some blood off my face. Then she kissed the clean spot. Simultaneously we looked at our hands; mine were thin and scarred and there was a bruise around the knuckle that had touched Rex's face; hers were short-nailed and capable-looking. She made a fist and the nicotine-stained fingers gleamed like metal.

'Go on,' she said. 'Dig.'

17

IT took about an hour to get the first brick out, but work went faster after that. I scraped and dug until the pain from my ribs and knee got too much and I had to hand over to Ann, who went at it furiously. She wanted to live very badly. After one session she wiped the sweat away and said savagely, 'You had a gun. Why didn't you shoot him?'

'He had a bigger gun,' I said.

We didn't talk much after that. I wondered how long it would take Manny to give pills to all the wrecks inside and I prayed that the van, wherever and whatever it was, would be slow to start. I scraped and dug.

We moved the dislodged bricks inside to cut down on the noise and I thought I'd at least have something to throw, if it came to that. When the hole was big enough, I told Ann to get to a phone and call the police.

'Scream at them,' I said. 'Panic them, tell them to bring everyone.'

'I will, don't worry.' She was halfway through when she asked, 'What about you?'

'I wouldn't get through the hole with this leg. Go, for Christ's sake!'

She kissed me again, quick and hard, wriggled through and started off; I think she'd have charged the shotgun if she'd had to. I dug out more bricks and got a hole big enough for my broad, manly shoulders. I tried to crawl through but I couldn't get the leverage with the bad knee.

So I sat there with a couple of half-bricks to hand, feeling like the boy with his finger in the dike. I turned the light off and I had a torch to dazzle him with, but he had a torch, too. If he came, I'd be like a blind kitten waiting to be drowned. I didn't want it to happen for all the usual reasons, and because of Bruce Henneberry who'd never write his articles now because of me. Ordinarily I'd have worried about my knee, which was locked and painful, but I was too worried about the rest of me.

Manny came, but when he did the night was full of sirens and shouts and blinking blue lights. I stuck my head out of the hole and saw him running down the path towards the cellar; lights flashed at him and he let go twice with the pump. The noise bounced off the buildings and roared down into the hole where I crouched with my half-bricks. Manny fired again and he was very close now. Somebody shouted 'Stop!' and he turned to see how far he'd got. The light lost him; I flicked on the torch and put the beam up on his chest. The shots were sharp and clean after the muffled boom of the shotgun. The first one took him high in the chest and he spun half around; the next one got him low and he went down. The shotgun slammed into the wall just above the hole.

I moved the torch beam around until I found his face, which was turned towards the wall. The hardness went out of it; his mouth relaxed and his fierce, slanting eyes dimmed and took on a fixed stare. Then blood flowed from his mouth, he gasped twice and he died.

I was shaking when they came for me. I felt cold right through and I thought I was going to have trouble keeping my pants dry. Parker crouched at the hole.

'Hardy, you okay?'

'Yeah. Grab his key and get me out of here.'

He burrowed into Manny's pockets, showing him as much respect as you'd show a scarecrow. He got a lot of blood on his hands, but he also got the keys and opened the door.

'What's that?' He'd turned on the light and pointed at the tub.

'Glue factory. They've been boiling down the senior citizens. See the tools outside? They're for burying the hard bits.'

'Shit! Can you stand up?'

'No. Can you get me some brandy or something?'

He yelled for assistance. The noise felt like a rain of bricks

on my head, but a bottle came. I took a pull on it; it wasn't
French, but it did something for that spreading cold.

'Did you get the other one—the woman?'

'No.'

'In a van.'

'No van.'

'She'll see all this a mile off. She runs this bloody place.'

'We'll get her. Take it easy.' He yelled again and I heard the
word 'ambulance'.

'What happened to your face?' He lit a cigarette and I didn't
want one.

'What's wrong with it?'

'Looks like you took on Sugar Ray Leonard.'

'That bad?' I was sweating and cold, scared and angry at the
same time. I groaned and heard the whine in my voice. 'Studded belt. Shit.' I ran my tongue around inside my mouth but
there was no extra damage there.

'Where am I bleeding?'

'Ear,' he said. 'Torn pretty bad.'

'Did Ann fill you in? Where is she?'

'Yeah, enough. She's okay. Is this where the guy you're looking for ended up?'

'Looks like it.'

He prowled about, puffing on his cigarette. A man came down
and whispered something to him and he issued instructions
about ambulances and hospitals.

'They're in a bad way up there,' he said.

'Yeah. Frank, get a spade and poke around in the garden. Use
my torch.'

He took the torch and went out. Stretcher-bearers arrived
and lifted me aboard. I clenched my teeth against the pain.

One of them took the bottle from me and said, 'Who gave
him this?'

'St Bernard,' I said. I was feeling lightheaded and had a crazy
impulse to wave my arms around. Ann Winter's face swam up
and I tried to smile at it, but blood dripped into my mouth.

'God,' she said.

They carried me out and made the turn to go up the path. I could see the light weaving about in the shrubbery and heard the spade bite into the earth.

'Wait,' I said. 'Frank?'

His voice sounded as if he had a mouthful of ground glass. 'Christ,' he said. 'It's a fucking graveyard.'

18

I WAS in hospital a week, and if I had had to pay my own bills it would have meant that I would have just about broken even on the Singer case. It's a muzzy professional and ethical area, medical bills run up in the course of duty. It's not wise to mention them in the initial interview in case you look accident-prone, but failure to do so can lead to unpleasantness later.

Anyway, they stitched up my ear without any trouble and put a few other stitches in my face, which would add to my tally of fetching scars in time. I had two broken ribs; again, time heals. The knee was the problem: there was ligament damage and chipped bone to worry about. An operation looked likely for a while, and I didn't fancy that. I never heard of anyone who'd had an operation on his knee ever being any good at what he did again. Eventually they decided to leave it alone and let physiotherapy and clean living repair the damage.

The cops came and took a detailed statement. Frank Parker visited and was almost non-official for ten minutes or so. Hilde visited, Ann Winter called in and one of their visits coincided. They got along very well.

'She's a beautiful girl, your lodger,' Ann said. Hilde had left after delivering a clean nightshirt and *Garp*. It was two days before I left hospital; I was sitting up in a chair and I had a stick to walk with. With the bandaged ear and all I thought I looked pretty dashing, very World War II and Battle of Britain.

"D'you reckon?"

'Yes. What a beautiful skin.' The way she said it made me wonder about Ann Winter. She seemed much more interested in Hilde's beautiful German skin than in dashing old me.

I'd made the hospital staff's lives miserable until they gave me a telephone. I rang Mrs Singer and her voice on the line was cool, or cooler.

'I've had a spot of bother,' I said.

'I read about it.'

The story of the old people held in captivity and defrauded of their pensions had had a long run in the papers. The tabloids had eked it out for days and one of them had come up with 'The Black Hole of Clovelly'. With some relatives who came to light and the investigations by the Social Security people, who were turning up a three-or four-year history, there was a major paper-selling item. A lot of bones and skulls had been found in the backyard and analysis was proceeding.

'Mrs Singer, we need to break confidentiality, at least a little.'

'Why?'

'I want you to arrange to release your husband's dental records to the police. I'll try to keep it as quiet as I can, but a technician or two might find out what's going on.'

She was silent.

'I take it your husband did go to the dentist in the time you knew him?'

'Twice, I think.'

'That'll do. Will you do what I say?'

'Of course.' I thought I detected some relief in her voice; certainly, she sounded less hostile. 'You don't really expect John to have been one of the victims, do you?'

'Why not?'

'It's fantastic.'

'You're right, it is. You saw the papers. One of the men in there had been a QC.'

'You're right, Mr Hardy. I'll contact the dentist.'

'Tell him to get the records to Detective Frank Parker with a covering note stressing confidentiality.'

I rang off; it wasn't the moment to try her out on the medical expenses. I couldn't gauge her reaction. She didn't seem to take the dental check very seriously and I didn't know how serious about it I was myself. It would be a neat ending but somehow I hated to think of anyone I'd been connected with, even indirectly, finishing up as one of Manny and Mahoud's discards.

I needn't have worried. Frank rang me the day I got home. I was installed on the couch downstairs with the phone to hand.

'How's the hero?'

'Crippled. Doubt if I'll ever hurdle again.'

'Tough. Brace yourself, Hardy. We checked your chopper charts.'

'And?'

'First place, the skulls were mostly female; only two men. Second place, no Singer. Nothing like it.'

'No mistakes? Good man on the job?'

'The best. No mistakes. The soil of Clovelly is a great preserver.'

'I've still got a case, then.'

'Yeah. Who's interested in Singer, if I may ask?'

'Wife. D'you know anything about it?'

'No, but I'll tell you what I'll do. I'll pull the file and take a look. Anything interesting I'll pass on.'

'Thanks, Frank. Any sign of Mahoud?'

'No. You mentioned money in the house in your statement.'

'Right. She tried to buy me off with it. I didn't find any, but I didn't do a complete search.'

'We did. No money. Could she have been lying?'

I thought back to the waves of desperation coming from behind that locked door. 'I don't think so. Looks like she took off with it.'

'Could have been a bundle. Kertez had a fair bit in the bank, but nothing like what they were making.'

'Who?'

'Kertez, Manfred Kertez. The late Manfred.'

'Oh.' I shifted on the couch as the knee gave me a twinge. 'The late' tag was comforting; I'd had one nightmare about being alone in a forest with Manny and his shotgun. There had been snow and I had had no shoes; it must have all been terribly Freudian, but that didn't help.

'With a lot of money she'll be hard to catch,' I said.

'True. Well, we shut the place down and we can close the file on Henneberry. Did you see the knife?'

'I saw it.'

'It checks out. The senator's happy . . . well, you know what I mean.'

'When can you get back to me on the Singer file?'

'This arvo.'

I rang Mrs Singer with the good news, if that's what it was.

'I'm not in the least surprised,' she said. 'Will you keep looking?'

'I'm just out of hospital. I've got a bad knee and a very big hospital bill.'

'I'll pay the bill. Will you keep on?'

'Yes.'

I used the stick and the furniture to get out to the kitchen for a drop of wine and a bit of cheese to aid thought. I was back on square one unless something in the police file on Singer put me on square two.

I propped myself against the window frame in the front room and looked out. Good blue sky, bit of wind in the trees, ideal day for almost anything. I opened the door and hobbled down to the letter box. There was nothing there, but I liked the feeling of independence. I looked carefully up and down the street. My neighbour Harry Soames had a visitor who drove a jeep; a liquor store was delivering to a house across the road; the dog from the house on the corner was curled up asleep on the bonnet of a Holden. I could see his muddy paw marks on the roof. There were no suspicious-looking technicians working in the street, none up poles or down holes. I doubted that Freddy Ward would have the pull to get my phone tapped, but anything is possible. As I limped back to the house I reflected that if Ward was still interested in me I was probably on square three, more exposed and vulnerable than two.

Frank rang in the early afternoon and was properly cautious.

'You'd better ask me questions, Hardy. I'll give you what I can.'

'Did anything point to Singer being murdered?'

'No, but nothing pointed to anything. Shit, he could be in Brazil. There's one thing you mightn't know, though. Singer

116

took a trip to the US a few weeks before he disappeared. Bit of a mystery about what he did there.'

'Interesting. Any chance of looking into it?'

'Why don't you? Wouldn't she kick in for a trip to Los Angeles?'

I let myself think about it for maybe thirty seconds. There was the international connection, of course—the ashram, Bruce Henneberry. But I knew it wasn't on. The answer lay here in Sydney, or there wasn't one. 'No, I don't think I can promote myself a trip to LA out of it.'

'Pity. Well, I can try.'

'Thanks. Whose movements were checked when it happened?'

'The wife's. All clear. Freddy Ward at his place in the country. Tom McLeary; movements accounted for by employees— not too firm, that. A few others—guy who worked on Singer's yacht, an old girlfriend—all okay.'

'Can I have the names and addresses?'

'Sure.' He read them off.

'Listen, Frank, how many people know that those dental records were Singer's?'

'Just me. I photocopied the dentist's stuff and blanked out the name. Standard procedure. Why?'

'I'd like to keep it that way. Not knowing who I was working for gave me an edge on Ward and I'd like to keep it.'

'You think Freddy Ward killed Singer?'

'I don't know.'

'What're you going to do now?'

'I don't know.'

'You're lucky you don't have to write reports.'

'I know that. I think of it every month when I can't meet the mortgage.'

'I can't meet the mortgage, either.'

'You smoke', I said. 'I don't.'

'I'm stopping. Today.'

'Bet you don't.'

'You're on. What'll it be?'

'A bottle of Glenlivet.'

'How long do I have to go?'

'I'll pay in a fortnight for a clean slate.'

'How do I prove it?'

'I'll ask Policewoman Reynolds.'

He snorted at that and rang off, but I thought I had a bet. Also I *did* know what I was going to do next—investigate privately, and that meant without telling Frank Parker.

I rang Ann Winter at Bondi and the whisky voice gave me the number for Point Piper.

'How's your knee?' she said.

'Fair. I can just get around with a stick.'

'Your stocks are high out Bondi way just now. Do you fancy older women?'

I thought about it. 'Depends on who they're older than.'

'I know a few who'd give you a good time. That Clovelly place really gave them the horrors.'

'Me, too. Listen, Ann, I want to talk to that woman who was at the wake. The one in the pink who said she knew the Singers. Where can I find her?'

She answered immediately. 'Back bar of the Royal Oak in Randwick.'

I was working again.

19

I WAS under strict medical instructions not to move around
more than necessary, but who ever took any notice of strict
medical instructions? When I see a rise in the percentage of
thin, fit doctors, I'll start paying more attention to their strict
instructions. Besides, the physical good I might have got by sitting on my bum at home would have been countered by the
emotional disturbance. I had to know what was going on. I took
a few red Codrals for the pain and put myself and my stick in
a taxi. First stop was the bank for cash in various denomi-
nations, then Randwick.

The taxi driver naturally assumed I was going to the races
and that I was a man of leisure.

'Got anything good?' He spoke with the mixture of respect
and distrust a working man feels for someone who comes out
of his house casually dressed in the middle of a weekday. I hadn't
looked at the horses since the Singer case started.

'Is Roderick Dhu running?'

'Yeah,' he said. 'In the fourth.'

The horse was trained by a friend of mine, an ex-boxer who
hardly ever fought an honest fight or ran a dishonest horse. 'Get
on that, each way.'

The Royal Oaks is just far enough from the track for someone to walk over, forget his or her losses and think about punt-
ing another day. I limped from the taxi into the back bar,
knocked the knee on a chair and was glad to get up on a bar
stool and start work on a scotch. The lady in pink was there
all right, in mauve that day, drinking and smoking in an experienced sort of way. She had a companion who looked middle-
aged, but after Ann's revelation of my subject's age I was not
confident about reading how many years these women had on

the clock. She wasn't young. They were both blowing the smoke around and not talking much; it didn't look like anything that couldn't be broken up with a little money. Ann had told me that she was going by the name of Peggy Harrison just then and that old Peg was a barrel of fun.

They finished the round and the companion came up to the bar and bought the next one. I drank slowly and when Peggy came up for her shout I had a ten-dollar note out and flapping in the breeze.

'Peggy?' I said.

'Two Bacardis and coke, sport,' she said to the barman, then she turned a magnificently bloodshot eye at me. 'Yes? Do I know you?'

'I was at Leon's wake with Ann Winter.'

The drinks came and naturally that was what she was most interested in. She grabbed them with the excessive caution of someone who has a slight load on board. But she'd caught sight of the ten.

'Nice girl, Ann.'

'Yes. Would this buy a little information?' I nudged the note. The barman was interested and trying to hover within earshot. I looked at him as if he had something in his nose and he backed off.

'Depends.' Her mate shouted, 'Peg!' from across the room and Peg ducked her head at her angrily. Peg's hair was dyed red, she wore a lot of makeup and her body was strapped in tight. She looked as if she'd spent a little money on herself since I'd last seen her. 'Depends,' she repeated. 'It might buy a little bit of some information.'

I took out another ten. 'Get rid of your friend and we'll have a chat.'

The friend didn't like it much, but she put her Bacardi down fast and went out. I walked across to the table with my second scotch and a fresh Bacardi.

'Cripple, are you?'

'Just temporary,' I said. 'Hang gliding.' I gave her the twenty dollars straight off and she offered me a menthol cigarette in return. I refused.

She sucked in the smoke. 'Safer than hang gliding.' She gave the sort of cackle that no person under sixty should be able to produce. Where the makeup had flaked off, her skin was a raddled ruin; her hair was thin and retreating like Glenda Jackson's as Elizabeth I, and all the alcohol and tobacco on her breath couldn't disguise the smell of poor teeth and lousy food. But through all that you could see she had once been beautiful, that her ruined features had once had a sort of perfection. And she still had guts.

'Don't look at me,' she said sharply. 'I look like garbage. What d'you want from me?'

She pulled hard on the cigarette and took a deep drink as if she wanted to hasten the decay.

'Singer,' I said. 'John Singer and his wife. I understand you know a bit about them.'

'Knew. Singer's dead.'

'Okay, knew.'

'Any more money?'

'It's my turn to say "It depends", Peggy. I'll pay well for something interesting.' I tapped her glass. 'Bit flush, aren't you?'

She sighed. 'Good double and had both of 'em each way. Once in a bloody blue moon. Nearly all gone now. What's your game?'

'Private investigator. Did you read about that house in Clovelly?'

She was wearing a thin yellow cardigan draped over her shoulders. She pulled the sleeves across her chest and shivered. 'I read about it.'

'I helped close it down. That's where I got the dicky knee.'

'You must be all right, then. Shit, what a place! Were they really . . . '

I didn't want to go down memory lane so I cut her off. 'The Singers, Peggy. What do you know?'

'I know a bit.'

'How come?' I hadn't meant to let the implication slip in—that she was light years removed from the Singers socially and financially, but she was smart and she caught it.

'I'm a mess, I know. Wasn't always. But my girl Sandy was on with Singer for a year or more. Then he dumped her. She was just a kid, eighteen or so, and she took it bad.'

'Singer'd be a bit long in the tooth for an eighteen-year-old, wouldn't he?' I said sceptically.

She finished her drink. 'Didn't look it, didn't act it. Sandy had no complaints, not at first. What're you drinking?' She got up with one of my tens in her hand. That's where it would go, dollar by dollar.

'Scotch.' My knee was hurting. When she came back with the drinks, she gave me a smile that still had a trace of the old power in it, but it would be a sloppy grimace soon.

'Singer wasn't so bad himself,' she said as soon as she'd lit another cigarette. 'Gave Sandy plenty of money, bought her a car. It was that bitch of a wife who was the real trouble.'

I sipped my drink and let her tell it.

'I got this from Sandy, see? She said something happened to Singer. He lost his . . . don't know what you'd call it. He couldn't get it up. All that. Depression, isn't that what they call it? Sandy reckoned the wife was behind it, driving him mad. Hard bitch.'

'Do you know her?'

'Yeah, I did. She's older than me but I don't suppose she looks it. Well, she knocked around a bit before she got on to Singer. I knew her then and for a few years after that.' Her voice trailed off. They would have been the bad years, when things started to slide and people started to avoid her and every problem needed two or three drinks instead of one. She snapped back to the present. 'I tell you she's as hard as they come. Singer always liked the girls, see? And Marion used to sort them out. I saw her do it once at a party. Bloody near ripped this kid apart.'

'How d'you mean?'

'Like this.' She made claws of her fingers and lifted them. The skin on her hands was yellow and cracked, her nails were bright red and some of the paint had got on the skin around them. She made a slashing movement and I got the idea. It was disconcerting stuff for a loyal and faithful employee to hear

122

about the boss. If Mrs S had turned the violence against the philanderer that would explain why Singer wasn't out boating and banging the birds any more. But it wouldn't explain calling me in. I was aware again of how much I didn't know about Singer; too much. That set me to thinking about people who would have known him.

'McLeary,' I muttered into my scotch.

'What?'

'Talking to myself. You're the first person I've talked to who's known anything much about Singer. I was thinking that Tom McLeary'd know a bit.'

'I'll say, but don't mention him and Marion Singer in the same breath.'

'Why?'

'Jesus! She hates him. He used to supply Singer with girls and they had the casino deal. You know about that?' She looked at me shrewdly as she finished her drink. Her brain was probably only half working, but there was enough of it ticking over for her to know how deep the water was. She wagged a finger at me. 'You don't know. Knew you didn't.'

'Tell me, then.' I put twenty dollars on the table.

'No. Fuck you, ask the bloody coppers.'

She was a bit scared and the booze was getting to her. The last one had probably been a double and it was hitting hard, the way it does when the liver's shot. And she was probably due for her afternoon nap before starting on the evening session. It wasn't parfit or gentil helping her to oblivion but it's not a parfit, gentil world. I pushed the money towards her.

'Tell me a bit more about McLeary and tell me where I can find Sandy.'

She looked at me with those eyes that had stared into countless drinks. She wanted to say no, to tell me to keep my grubby questions away from the spotless ears of her little girl. She was a mother and an alcoholic and the body chemistry won. Besides, the ears weren't spotless any more.

'Get us another drink.' She held up her glass and I could feel her watching me as I limped away to get it. She could punish me just that much.

'Won't tell you much about Mac. In everything, gambling . . . Edgecliff, Maroubra . . . girls . . . papers.'

'What do you mean, papers?'

'Place is full of fuckin' foreigners. Wogs, chinks. Papers, passports, you know.'

I nodded. 'Sandy, and the name she goes by.'

'More money,' she said. More oblivion, more laughs, less pain.

I put another twenty on the table. She took the notes and her knuckles cracked as she closed her hand around them.

'Modesto,' she said.

I looked at her.

'Her father . . . bigger shit than Singer, bigger shit than you, biggest shit in the world.'

'Address?'

'Flat two, eighty-one Robbins Road, Double Bay.'

It was a different address, but the name Modesto was the one Frank Parker had given me as the girlfriend whose movements had been checked.

'What does she do?' I said.

She shrugged.

'Has she got a friend?'

'Yeah, Yank. Funny name, Tod or somethin'. Piss off.'

20

'FRANK, you've been holding out on me.' I was using a telephone in the Royal Oaks.

'Never.'

''Fraid so. You neglected to tell me about the casino deal.'

'Uh,' he said.

'Sounds pretty important to me. Now, did I or did I not help you to clear up two murders?'

'One. We never even opened a file on Leon.'

'One, then, but a good one.'

'Okay. It's a little difficult . . . ' He broke off and his voice had nothing of the special, concise, on-top-of-it-all Frank Parker tone. I guessed the reason.

'Your colleagues are in the room and you can't just shoot the breeze about casinos. Right?'

'Right.'

'We'll play it the way we played it before, only I'll ask the questions. Now, there was some sort of deal about the casinos that involves the constabulary. Yes?'

'That's so.'

'All I know is that they open and close. Let me guess; the deal takes in McLeary and Ward?'

'That's two out of three.'

'Singer?'

'Right.'

It gave the thing some shape and structure at last. The casinos were big money, very big, and big people were involved, political people. It was reasonable to suppose that Singer, Ward and McLeary had the go-ahead from the cops in some way. But what way? *Deal, deal, deal,* I thought. *What do deals involve? Time.*

'Are you still there, Hardy?'

'I'm here. The deal is for one operator to have an open go for a period of time.'

'Exactly right.'

'Whose turn is it now?'

'Moot point.'

'Who's doing it now?'

'Singer.'

'How long is the agreed period?'

'Two years.'

'So Singer's overdue to bow out?'

'Right again. We're talking about the wife.'

'Thanks, Frank. You're a real pal.'

'Don't get too smart, Hardy. It's tricky country.'

'Just where do you stand on it, Frank? I know you've got judges playing blackjack and shadow ministers putting their shirts on the red, but it'd help to know what your considered attitude is.'

He spoke slowly and it was obvious that he'd thought it over many times. 'Pending legalisation,' he said, 'I'm for a little rationalisation.'

'Am I to understand that there's been trouble at handing-over time in the past?'

'Absolutely.'

'I think I can help you.'

'This conversation never happened.' Good old Frank. He'd extend his neck an inch or so but he wouldn't stick it all the way out. He was right, of course; banks and insurance companies employ lots of ex-cops who've spoken out of turn.

'We have an understanding,' I said. 'See you soon.'

Double Bay is hilly; very bad for a man with a crook leg, very good for property developers. It's also good for hairdressers, couturiers and people who sell tiny pictures widely bordered by snowy white paper and enclosed in the slimmest of frames. A lot of media people living there kid themselves that they can walk to work in town. Usually they drive. The cars of Double Bay are a study in themselves. On a car-for-car basis, Japan and Germany won World War II and neutrality paid off big for Sweden.

Robbins Road goes up and down dramatically in a couple of hundred yards. The taxi dropped me at the end of the road and I discovered the first law of walking with a stiff knee—it's a hell of a lot easier to walk uphill than down. Swinging the stiff leg up, you can sort of place it gently; coming down the grade you tend to thump it into place. The jar goes up the bone to the knee and the nerves do the rest. So you tend to go downhill crabwise—very slow and undignified.

Number eighty-one was a newish block, a modish five storeys with some nice shrubbery around it. There would be no change out of eight hundred bucks a month for a flat. I went up the path hoping to find flat two on the ground floor, but it was one flight up. I was sweating and gritting my teeth when I got there. Life's a gamble, but I hoped like hell Sandy was at home. The door was a sophisticated job with an unpickable lock; kicking it in wasn't on just then. As I pressed the buzzer, I wondered about Sandy: Singer had dropped her just over two years before when she had been eighteen. That made her twenty or so now. Twenty can be nursery-school callow or as hard as Ilse Koch.

The woman who answered the bell was Peggy cast back twenty years. She had thick, lustrous red hair, thin, arched eyebrows and a face that would have made John Singer feel years younger than he was. One of the eyebrows went up with practised slowness.

'Mmm?'

'I've just come from talking to your Mum in the Royal Oaks. I gave her fifty dollars and she gave me your address. I'll make it up to a hundred for her or give it to you if you'll give me half an hour of your time.'

She looked at me curiously through the eight-inch gap allowed by the security chain.

'What would Peggy have worth fifty dollars?'

'I'll tell you if you'll open the door.'

She was a careful lady; she looked me over from top to bottom. I was still wearing a heavy bandage around my ear and

127

the top of my head. Peggy hadn't commented on it, but I suppose she was used to people falling over and hurting themselves. That plus my hospital pallor might give me an air of fragility that would encourage Sandy to let me in. I leaned heavily on the stick for emphasis.

'What's the stick for?'

'I hurt my leg. I barely got up the stairs and it pains me just standing here.'

'You might attack me with it.'

I laughed. 'You'd beat me. I can hardly move without it, but I'll leave it out here if it worries you.' I leaned the stick against the wall and got out my licence, letting her see some money sitting in there with it. 'I'm a private detective. You can call Detective Frank Parker at College Street headquarters to check me if you want to. I don't attack women.'

It was her turn to laugh. It was a good Sydney sound that suggested she'd had more good times than bad so far.

'I suppose it's all right.' She unfastened the chain. 'My boyfriend's due in half an hour, anyway.'

'Thanks.' I limped into the hallway and steadied myself against the wall.

'Get the stick, for God's sake.' It wasn't a bad voice she had; very contemporary, using the rising inflection, but not on every group of words. I got the stick and went down the hall into the living-room. The apartment had big windows which were making the most of the afternoon light. The fittings were good but unremarkable, except for a very nice Persian carpet. There was a big TV set and a lot of silver-banded hi-fi equipment. No books. A gold steering wheel was mounted on a block of wood and the whole thing was about nine inches high, standing on top of the TV set. She saw me looking at it.

'He's a racing car driver, my boyfriend.'

I nodded and eased myself down into the chair with the most padding.

'I didn't catch your name.'

'Cliff Hardy. I'm interested in John Singer. I can't tell you why.'

'That'd be right,' she said. She got a Benson and Hedges Extra Mild out of its box and lit it with a gold lighter. 'What do you want for the fifty dollars?'

'Tell me about how he went off you.'

It wasn't polite and she didn't like it, but I wasn't going to get anywhere by being too polite with Sandy. The eyebrows and the way she smoked and moved told me that she was a long way from being a kindergarten teacher. She was a woman who'd been valued and who had accepted the going rate. She frowned and tapped ash off the Benson and Hedges.

'Peggy told you that?'

'Yes.'

'How's Peggy? I haven't seen her for a while.'

I opened my hands. 'She's okay, I guess. Won a bit on the horses, she said. Drinking Bacardi.'

'That's her drink when she's got money.' She stood and leaned over to crush out her cigarette. She was medium tall with a good figure; her breasts under a black V-neck sweater fell forward heavily when she leaned down. Nothing heavy about the rest of her; she was trim-hipped and snappy as she turned towards a door. 'Want a drink?'

'No, thanks. Don't stall me. Are you going to talk to me about Singer or not?'

She went out of the room and I heard drink-making noises. 'How do I know she'll get the money?'

'I said I'd give it to you if you wanted it.'

She came back carrying what looked like a gin and tonic and sat down on a couch opposite me. She sipped the drink. 'No, give it to her.' There were a lot of things in the order—affection, disappointment and disgust as well. She worked on her drink and got another smoke going. Mother's girl.

'I liked John,' she said softly. 'He was good to me. I was in a bad way when I met him.' She pointed a long, elegant finger at the Persian carpet. 'Going down fast, you know? He fixed me up, we had a flat, went out a bit. Good times. He was very, very smart, the smartest man I ever met.'

'How do you mean, smart?

129

'Like, he figured everything out in advance. He'd say, we'll do this and this and then this'll happen. And it always did. We had a bit of trouble getting clear of Mac. Have you heard of him?'

I nodded.

'Well, he had a sort of hold on me, but John outsmarted him.'

'I get it. How long were you on with him?'

'A year, bit less.' She raised a finger to her mouth as if she was going to bite the nail, but pulled it away sharply and took a drink instead.

'What happened to him?'

'He just went limp. He wasn't the same, wouldn't talk, no more jokes. He seemed to spend all his time thinking.'

'What about?'

'No idea. He hardly talked to me at all. I thought Marion was giving him hell about us.'

'Do you know that for sure?'

'No. But what else could it have been?'

'Was he sick?'

'He was never sick. Fit. You know?'

Fit, I thought, *fit, rich and smart. So what went wrong?*

'Peggy said he was impotent.'

She laughed, a touch brutally, as if she had to toughen herself up to talk about this subject. 'I bet she didn't say that. True, though. He couldn't do it. He gave me a car—I've still got it— and some money. He paid three months on the flat and that was it. He didn't explain. I called him everything, but it made no bloody difference.'

'Did you ever travel with him?' I asked abruptly.

'Sure. Queensland . . . '

'I mean overseas.'

'Japan once.'

'He went to the States, didn't he?'

'Couple of times. No, I didn't go.'

The shadows were lengthening on the carpet, deepening the dark blues and reds, and a deep bronze patch glowed in the fading light. A shaft of sun through the clouds and through the window caught on the ornament on top of the TV and made it shimmer. The golden wheel seemed to turn slowly as the light caught it.

I peeled off fifty dollars and put them on the arm of the chair. Mrs Singer's bill was going to be high. That made me think of the hospital account, and maybe it was that which caused my knee to give a severe twinge. I bit my lip.

'You all right?'

'Yeah. Have you got any painkillers? I left mine at home.'

'You don't want a joint? Great for pain.'

I smiled. 'You're a drug fiend, too?'

She had her handsome face ready for a friendly expression, but it dropped away. 'What d'you mean, *too*?'

It had slipped out. I was so used to needling people, catching them on the raw, that I'd said it automatically. She wasn't living in a flat with a Persian carpet and five thousand dollars worth of woofers and tweeters on the money John Singer had given her two years before. But it was no business of mine.

'Nothing,' I said. 'Have you got a pill?'

'I'll see,' she said coldly. She walked out and I heard her banging cupboards and drawers. The knee was stiffening and getting sore; I got the stick and stood up to loosen it. I hobbled over to the television set and picked up the ornament. It was trophy time again. Every man should have at least one trophy. I used to have one at home myself, a little job: 'Runner-up High Schools 4 x 220 yards'. I ran third leg and lost some ground that the fourth man made up. A long time ago.

The doorbell rang and Sandy ran through the room and down the hall. She didn't seem to be worried about her boyfriend finding her with a strange man and fifty bucks in a neat pile on a chair arm. I looked again at the plaque mounted on the ornament, unshipped my .38 and got it ready to shoot. The front door closed and when they got into the living-room, I had it pointed at his chest. I tossed the mounted steering wheel across at him.

'Hello, Tal,' I said.

21

TALBOT Brown, winner of the Philadelphia Stockcar Grand
Prix in 1976, used both hands to catch his trophy. He
hugged it to his chest and spoke in his soft accent.

'Boy, oh boy. Are you in trouble.'

I raised the gun a fraction. Sandy jumped and drew closer to
Brown; for a second I thought she was going to slip in behind
him. 'I'd say *you* were in trouble, Talbot,' I said. 'I still owe you
a few from last week.'

I limped away from the window to take up the dominating
position in the room, which is always in the centre and a little
to the back. He watched me critically.

'We didn't do that,' he said.

'No, I met up with someone tougher than Rex.'

'I'm real glad to hear it.'

'He's dead now, of course.'

Smartarse stuff, but it's sometimes like that. The guns are
almost comic until they go off. I never heard anyone laugh
straight after a gun went off. Sandy didn't know the rules. She
moved forward sharply which caused me to jerk the gun at her.

'What the hell *is* this?' She screeched. 'Tal, do you know this
man? What's the gun . . .'

Her alarm made me nervous. 'Shut up!' I snapped. 'You've
really been the rounds with this mob, haven't you, Sandy?
McLeary, Singer and now Freddy Ward's chauffeur. Coming
down in the world, though.'

Brown moved forward a step and transferred the trophy to
his right hand.

'Put it down gently, Tal,' I said. 'We don't want to break it.
Do it or I'll shoot you. I mean it!'

He did it. Rex would have been in pretty bad shape when

132

they found him and minus his big gun as well. That must have earned me a little respect, but I couldn't afford to lose a fraction of it.

'Right,' I said. 'Now sit down and let's keep it friendly. You tell me what I want to know and nobody gets hurt. If you don't, I won't be answerable. This leg makes me very bad-tempered. How's Rex, by the way?'

He sat down on the edge of a chair, hitching at his pants a bit as he did it. His black beard was carefully trimmed and didn't look as if it hid a weak chin as my father always opined beards did. He had been wrong about a lot of things. Tal didn't look quite as wide out of his overalls, but he was wide enough. He was wearing a blue suit with a blue and white wide-striped shirt under it. I picked out the point on the stripe I'd have to hit to stop him.

'Rex is real anxious to meet you again,' he said.

'I'll bet. Sandy, you mentioned a drink before. And did you find any painkillers?'

She looked at Brown, who nodded impatiently. 'How did you take Rex? He wouldn't tell us. And what did you do with his gun? He was crazy about that weapon.'

'I took him with a bit of string and a hell of a lot of luck. I'd say Rex was an unlucky type. He should be in a different line of work. I gave his gun to the cops.'

He looked surprised at that and not pleased.

'I never knew a driver who was any good with a gun. Have you got one, Tal?'

'No.'

'Good. You know, I saw a pump shotgun the other day. Belonged to the guy who gave me this leg. If I had it here I could demonstrate what it can do. I should have souvenired it. It'd knock that fancy TV set through the wall, for a start.'

Sandy had been clinking things in the kitchen. She came in with a tray and nearly dropped it when she heard me. There was a bottle of Teacher's scotch on the tray with some glasses and a bowl of ice. She'd filled a milk bottle with water and it rattled against a glass as she put the tray down. A strip of Aspros was beside the scotch.

Tal didn't look too comfortable; he glanced at my head bandage a couple of times as if he was wondering whether I'd suffered brain damage. That was all right with me.

I'll take four Aspros,' I said to Sandy. She peeled the paper off. 'And a bit of the Teacher's with water. Keep to one side as you do it!'

I sat down in the chair with the money on it and sipped my drink while she poured two more. She sat down; I put my glass down, picked up the money and flicked it at her. The notes fell untidily on the Persian carpet.

'What's that for?' Tal asked, and his accent was a little less soft.

'Information,' I said. 'Like what you're going to give me, except that I'm not going to pay for it.'

'Get fucked.' He was lifting his glass to his mouth. I swung the stick and the metal ferrule hit it just right—the glass shattered and the liquid sprayed all over him. Sandy shrieked and dropped her drink.

'A waste,' I said. 'And bloody bad for the carpet.' I put the stick down, keeping the gun steady, and had a drink. I crumbled two of the Aspros in my fingers and put the powder into the glass.

'My leg hurts. And I'm nervous, and I don't like people who kick me. As I said, you're in trouble.'

'He's mad,' Sandy whispered.

'I told you to get fucked.' He was picking glass out of his clothes. His trousers were wet at the thighs and a little cut on his cheek just above the beard was bleeding. A sliver of glass caught in the dark beard glittered like a gem. Adrenalin was rushing through me and my mind was speeding, but I reckoned I didn't have long in the cockpit. The phone could ring; someone could call. Tal was genuinely tough and resourceful the way racing drivers have to be. He'd try something.

'I won't try to be reasonable with you,' I said. 'Racing drivers are fucking lunatics to start with. I want to know why Freddy Ward was so interested in me.'

134

His mouth started to form those same words again and I tapped him on the knee with the stick, not hard, not soft. 'I learned a bit about knees in the hospital. How they work, and all. Tricky things, easy to hurt.' I whacked the side of the same knee. He winced and swore.

'Knees and eyes,' I said. 'That's what a driver needs. I guess hands aren't so important.' His hand was resting on the arm of the chair and I slammed the stick down on it. He yelped and wrung the hand.

I kept my eyes locked on his and moved the gun up a bit. 'This is a Smith & Wesson Combat .38, two-inch barrel, six shots. But you won't have to worry about the six shots. I'm going to shoot you in the right knee, then I'm going to poke your left eye out with this.' I tapped the stick. 'With a bit of luck you'll still be able to drive—automatics.'

Sandy started to cry softly. 'I won't lay a finger on you,' I said. It was a crude hard-soft sell and I was using all the props I had. I kept tapping the stick and Sandy kept crying and it all got to Tal eventually.

'You wouldn't do it,' he said shakily.

'Why not?'

'You'd lose your licence.' It was a weak effort and he knew it. I grinned at him and moved the two-inch barrel forward one inch.

'You abducted me and beat me up. I've got a witness to the abduction and people saw me afterwards. Now, I'm in a hard game; if it got around that you did that to me and got away with it, I'd lose a lot of business. That's one thing. Another is that I've had a traumatic experience. You can see the bandages. I'm not quite right in the head, you might say. That's two. Last, who's on your side? Sandy might go to the cops, but she might not. I might lose the licence. I don't think so, but what difference would it make to you in your wheelchair? I'm finished talking, Tal. Last chance.'

'Okay, okay,' he said quickly. 'I'll tell you what I know.'

I took a sip of the scotch and couldn't taste it. 'Good. Don't bullshit me, or we're back where we started. I know there's politics in it, and the casinos. Let's take it on from there.'

He took a deep breath. 'There's this new area near Camden; what do you call it down here? A growth area? Freddy wants in with the massage parlours and the gambling. He's decentralising, but he's afraid he's losing his grip. I don't know much about the casino deal; it's some kind of three-way split and Freddy missed the boat. This Camden thing is real big for him. There's people don't like him and people who have to like him if he's going to get the action. He thought you might be working for someone who's trying to keep him out of this new spot.'

'How would I do that?'

'By digging up the dirt on his operations in the eastern suburbs and passing it on.'

'The cops know all about that.'

'It's not cops we're talking about.'

'Politicians?'

'Right.'

I let out a slow breath I hadn't meant to hold that long. 'What else?'

'Nothing. I swear it, Hardy. He needs to be Mr Clean for these political types.'

'Why? He's buying them, isn't he?'

'That's the way it works.'

I thought it over while he fidgeted. People don't like to see other people thinking. You never can tell which way thinking is going to pan out. I let him sweat. What he'd said sounded right. The new slums-to-be they called 'growth areas' were an open go. Fucking and gambling were the in-demand services; there wasn't much else to do in those dumps. You needed to fix some aldermen, which took more money than subtlety, and some of the next rank of politicians, which took a bit of both. Bill Anderson would be interested. I thought I knew how to use the information myself.

'Is Freddy Ward insane?'

The change of tack brought a look of relief to his face, which had been locked into a grimace of doubt. He dried his palms on his pants leg. Sandy was quiet.

'I wouldn't say that. You saw him. Look, I just drive for him; I don't talk to his goddamn doctor.'

He was getting cocky again and it was time for me to go. 'Okay, I believe you,' I said. 'I'll tell you something for free—Tom McLeary says Ward killed John Singer.'

'Jesus.' He looked quickly at Sandy.

'That's what Tom told me and what he's told a lot of people lately. Anything in it, d'you reckon?'

Brown shook his head slowly. 'Before my time.'

'Sandy?'

The tears had made her eyes shine and given her an innocent look she probably hadn't had since she was twelve.

'I don't know how John died. He was a wonderful swimmer. I don't see how he could have drowned.'

'That's what a lot of people think. Mac says Ward fixed it so he couldn't swim, but he could be wrong. Nasty rumour, though.'

I got up carefully, not putting too much weight on the stick and not letting anything deflect the gun. Tal was doing the thinking now and it didn't look as though he could do that and try rough stuff at the same time.

I went slowly past them and backed down the passage to the door. I closed it hard behind me and put my ear to it. The first sound I heard was the clink of a bottle against a glass; the second was the sound of a telephone dialling.

22

I HAD a slight relapse after this activity. The knee hurt like hell on the way down the stairs at Sandy's place, hurt in the taxi and felt as if someone was hammering four-inch nails into it when I got home. The hospital had given me some analgesics which I'd avoided, but I took them then. They wiped me out for hours and left me wakeful and fretful through the night. Hilde did some early-morning nursing and brought in a big cardboard box from the doorstep before leaving for her lectures. She looked, I noted resentfully, fresh, fit and cheerful.

'Something here for you to play with,' she said. 'Are you comfortable, Cliff?'

'Like a koala in a tree,' I growled. 'What's in the bloody box?'

She thumped it down on the floor beside the couch. 'I can hardly bear to leave all this joy and happiness. See you later, sunshine.'

I grunted and lifted the lid of the box. It contained knee-exercising gear—ropes, weights and pulleys—which the hospital was hiring out to me at some expense. Another bill for Mrs Singer. I'm not mechanically minded, and setting up the equipment taxed me. When it was assembled I set it to 'light work', put my foot in the sling and lifted. 'Light work' was quite heavy enough for the time being. 'Transverse movement' sounded a bit on the painful side. The equipment and the elastic bandage that had to be applied before using it took me back to my athletics days, to those third-leg relays and the long and high jumps that seemed to land me on rubbing tables as often as not. Football meant bruises and stitches, until it seemed that tennis was the only game I could play without injuring myself. Eventually I gave up trying to be Bob Matthias and with drinking, smoking and staying up late I got in good shape for snooker.

At mid-morning I got on the phone to Camden. After half an hour I located Bill Anderson at the school where he was teaching history.

'Hi,' he said. Another cheerful bastard. 'What's been happening?'

'Nothing much. I've got a line on the owner of that house and a few other details that might interest you.'

'Hang on.' The line hummed with background sounds—doors opening and closing, yawns and cups clinking.

'American history,' he said. 'I told them to check for lies in Nixon's inauguration address.'

'That's not history.'

'It is to them. They've never heard of him.'

'What about Roosevelt?'

'I asked them once. One of the smarter ones thought he was something to do with Breaker Morant. What've you got on mystery mansion?'

I filled him in on Ward's plans for the growth area and the way he was likely to go about them. I apologised for not knowing any of the names.

'Don't need 'em,' he said. 'Not hard to guess at a few. It's very interesting, Mr Hardy. Could help.'

'Cliff,' I said. 'How d'you look for the election?'

'Just fair. I'm not too worried. I'm having fun.'

I'd never heard a politician say he was having fun before. 'Would you like to do me another favour?'

'Sure.'

'I'm trying to stir the possum a bit. If you could drop the word that Tom McLeary says Freddy Ward bumped off John Singer, it'd help.'

'Ward responsible Singer murder according to McLeary. That it?'

'Yeah. Be subtle.'

'We've got a good bowling club out here. Is that the sort of place you'd like it dropped?'

'Exactly. And a pub or two.'

'You want to make sure it gets to the Lions and Rotary.'

'You've got the idea.'

He said he'd get on it after school, which meant after lunch. School teaching has changed; my teachers would never have said an American President lied, or have knocked off after lunch. Most of them had worn suits, they had all worn ties, and half of them had tried to pretend they had still been in the army.

I told Anderson I'd get on to my Aunt Lyndall and put her to work with her coffee circle. He asked me what I'd done with the gun and when I said I'd given it to the police he sounded happy.

Ann Winter was still at Point Piper and sounding defensive.

'I was thinking of coming over to see you,' she said. 'Is your lady there?'

'She's not my lady. Feel like slumming, do you?' I was at it again, needling unnecessarily.

'What's that supposed to mean, Hardy?' she snarled. I could picture her working with a thumbnail at the ragged end of one of her rollies and dropping ash on the shag pile.

'Nothing,' I said.

'Reckoned I've chucked it, do you? Stopping on here in Disneyland?' I didn't say anything and she went on, working herself up. 'I'm writing. Heard of that? Writing up? You do it away from the field. Malinowski didn't do it in the fucking Trobriands, he did it in London.'

'Ann, I'm sorry, I'm sorry. It's my knee, blame the knee. Listen, are you going back to Bondi soon?'

'Yes, I have to go back tonight for a bit. Some things I have to check. Oh, did you see Peg?'

'Yeah, I saw her. She was a big help. You could help me some more if you'd whisper around a certain canard.'

I heard her sigh on the line. 'You know, I could never decide whether I liked you or not, and I still can't.'

'You do,' I said. 'You like me. Besides, we saved each other's lives. It's a bond.'

'There's that, I suppose. What is it—the canard?'

'That Thomas McLeary says Freddy Ward killed John Singer.'

'Did he?'

'Did he what?'

'Kill him.'

'I thought you might be asking if McLeary said he did.'

'Oh, shit. Never mind. All right, if I get a chance I'll spread it.'

'Thanks. I'll take you out to dinner when this is all over and we'll talk about Radcliffe-Brown.'

'When will that be?'

'Soon.'

'Look after your other leg.' Click.

I'm not what you'd call a committee man. I get restless if I hear more than two people talking about the same subject because it's a fair bet that only one of them will be talking sense. So I don't like teamwork or sub-contracting and only do it when I have to.

Roger Wallace runs a big investigating agency in town and has tried to recruit me several times, without success. We preserve a mutual professional respect. I got past his secretary to a direct enjoyment of his successful voice.

'I heard you got thumped, Cliff,' he said.

'Kicked.'

'Not *there*, I hope.'

'No, Roger, not there.'

'Good. Well?'

'I need a house watched. Big place, out Camden way. Also a tail on one or two men. A phone call to me if there are interesting developments. No action.'

'Easy. Whose house?'

'Freddy Ward.'

'Freddy? How nice. He do the kicking?'

'No.'

'You surprise me. All right, you're on. Two men and they don't come cheap. How long?'

'Two days, three at most.'

'When do they start?'

'Now.' I gave him details of Ward's house and descriptions of Rex and Tal. I told him that there could be activity in Glebe and the eastern suburbs. He told me his chilling daily rate; I looked around my room that needed painting and wondered how much the agents got to keep.

By lunchtime I felt better. I scrambled some eggs, drank wine and soda and called Frank Parker inviting him over and asking him to bring a few things with him. While I waited I read some more of Hemingway's letters, which Hilde had given me in hospital. I was reflecting that I hadn't written a personal letter in years when Frank knocked.

'Nice dump,' Frank said when he got inside.

'You always say the right thing. Drink?'

He had one and put his feet on a chair. He was wearing a lightweight grey suit and a blue tie. He fiddled with the end of the tie.

'Not smoking?' I said.

'No. Get to the point, Hardy. Glebe is all greyhounds and trendies as far as I'm concerned, and I don't like either.'

'Right. I'm stirring up trouble between Freddy Ward and Tom McLeary.'

'Shouldn't be hard. Why?'

'To find out what happened to Singer.'

'They know?'

'Someone knows in that bloody troika, and I want to squeeze it out.'

'Troika? You count Mrs Singer in too?'

'Have to.'

'She hired you to find out.'

I leaned forward to pour him more wine. 'Maybe she put him through her blender and can't handle the guilt; I just don't know. But I reckon I can flush something out.'

He put his hand in his pocket and brought out a cylinder about the size of a nasal inhaler. He tossed it up and caught it. 'Why d'you want this?'

'I've got one more move to make. I have to front McLeary and twist his balls. That'll be dangerous and I'd like to have someone on hand to help.'

'We're understaffed.'

'You brought that. You're going to play along.'

'Yeah. Well, I can probably find a cadet to put on it. It's irregular, but everything's fucking irregular these days. Did you hear we're getting gay policemen?'

'You've already had them. It's just a matter of owning up.'

He looked sour at that; it was cigarette time, so he played with the cylinder. 'Pretty simple, this. It gives off a hum in the patrol car—directional. You flick this switch and it screams. Good for half a mile or so.' He threw it across and I caught it.

'Thanks. How many men can you spare?'

'I'll give you two for three days.'

'I'd rather have three for two days.'

'No.' He got up and stretched. 'Back to it. I'm looking forward to the Glenlivet.'

'You'll crack.'

'No,' he said, 'I won't.' I believed him. 'I'll put them on in the morning. That okay?'

I said it was, and opened the door for him.

'You'll have to think of somewhere to put that bleeper, Hardy. If you stick it up your arse you won't be able to work the switch.'

23

I READ, watched television, ate and used the knee exerciser. Hilde didn't come home; she doesn't always. I took the analgesics again and read Hemingway in the wee small hours. Tough luck, Scott, tough luck, Ernest. I thought about the Singer case and decided I'd handled it all wrong. I should have tried to find out in detail what sort of man Singer was; what he thought, what he did hour by hour. Then I might have been able to judge what he did to himself or what was done to him. But it was too late for that and the water was muddled. My present strategy was a Judas goat approach. I didn't like it, but it was all there was. Of course I could pull out altogether, declare a no-contest, but that wasn't on; I'd done it before and it left me with that feeling of being unable to recall a fact, but magnified a thousand times and intolerable.

Hilde came home in the morning and I sent her out to do a little shopping for me. It took her most of the morning and when she got back she poured herself a hefty glass of wine, a rare thing for her to do before six.

'Some men are watching the house,' she said.

'That'd be right. What do they look like?'

'I only caught a glimpse—moustaches and longish hair.' She touched the back of the collar of the shirt she was wearing. She had her hair up in a tight bun.

'That's okay,' I said. 'They're cops. It's the ones with the short hair and suits you have to worry about.'

She sniffed and drank some wine. I had a glass with her just to be companionable. I flexed the knee and thought it felt a bit firmer.

'What's happening, Cliff? Is it dangerous?

'Moderately. I'll take you out for a *sauerbraten* when it's all over.'

'I don't like *sauerbraten*.'

The second team of cops came on duty in the early evening; Frank had been better than his word. I rang Roger Wallace.

'Freddy's keeping it rural. He might be sighting in rifles, of course. One of his boys went into town and stomped around the beaches for a bit.'

'Is he back yet?'

'No.'

'I think there'll be action when he gets back. Let me know.'

He called back an hour later. 'Moving,' he said. 'Freddy and three others, two cars, heading for town.'

'Thanks, Roger. Send me the bill.'

Hilde had gone out to a film. She phoned as I'd asked and said she thought there were at least two suspicious-looking cars parked near the house. I asked her what film she was going to.

'*Gallipoli*.'

'My grandfather was there.'

'On which side?' she asked.

I got out the knee brace that Hilde had brought that morning. It was a revolting object with straps, flesh-coloured plastic and padding. It nauseated me to look at it, which was part of the idea. I slit the padding and tucked the little cylinder away, positioned so that I could get at the switch and look as if I was scratching my knee. The brace stiffened the knee and hurt, but all great planners have their problems. Think of Napoleon and his piles.

There was no point in putting it off. I left the house and limped along the street, trying to keep the end of the stick out of the dog shit. I made it to the Toxteth and had a beer in the half-empty bar. The television was on with a news report that a certain known criminal had been shot and killed by a certain known policeman. Everyone seemed to know everyone else—the crim's brother knew the copper who knew the crim's girlfriend.

'LA again?' the barman asked.

'Please.'

'What'd you do to your leg?'

I thought of saying, 'A ski-ing accident', and then I saw my face in the mirror behind the bar. The two grooves that ran down beside my nose seemed to be getting deeper and when I squinted to see better the crows' feet cracked and fissured beside my eyes. It wasn't a ski-ing face; it was an amateur boxing face, a square-bashing face, a worrying-about-the-prostate face. *Hell*, I thought. *I am putting it off.*

The street beside the Toxteth hotel is narrow and dark and leads down to the water. Not a very nice stretch of water. I was halfway down it when the car pulled in a few yards ahead of me. A man jumped out of the back seat and went behind me; the driver moved in to block me off. He had a good-sized gun in his hand; it was a bad light for shooting but the range was perfect. Unless I did a Fosdick flop over the car, they had me.

'Get in the car, Hardy,' Bob said.

He'd wanted to fight me way back on day one, and now he looked a little embarrassed to be holding a gun on a crippled man. He shoved it in his pocket and flexed a couple of muscles instead.

'How's Sharon?' I said.

He jerked his thumb rudely and I moved towards the car, which was a Commodore, not as roomy for my leg as the Caddy. I leaned on the stick while the second man opened the back door. He gave me a little push and relieved me of the stick as I stumbled in. He swung the stick and broke it on a brick pillar; the broken end snapped up and hit him in the face. I laughed and he swore. We weren't off to a good start, him and me.

He got in beside me, still swearing, and the gunman got behind the wheel.

'Where are we going?' I said.

My companion in the back told me to shut up. He had bad body odour and I was already sweating with fear. If we went very far, the back seat would smell like a truckie's crotch.

We rolled sedately down to the water and took the back way to Bridge Road. Bob picked up speed a bit around Wentworth Park and swung out fast into Wattle Street. He was driving over the speed limit, but not fast enough to raise a five-point alarm. I knocked my knee on one of the turns. Bob kept one eye on the rear vision mirror.

I reviewed my plan as he did his stuff and the atmosphere in the back of the car got richer. People like Ward, Singer and McLeary inhabit a world of their own. It has its own society and rules, meeting places and established procedures. You don't find out anything about it by hanging around the edges; you have to dive right into the middle of the steaming pile. I planned to accuse McLeary of killing Singer; if he took it seriously, that would mean something. Ward was already taking it seriously; the trick was to stay alive and to work out what the reactions meant. I had the cops and the bleeper as a safety net. It was crude, but so was Jack Dempsey's left hook.

The hard part was the fear. One part of me rejected all this and wanted escape via a magic lantern and three wishes. That part said, *To hell with Ward and McLeary and all the other scum that floats in the city*. This was the part that wondered why I didn't have the things other men had—degrees, a wife, superannuation. Against that was the vanity I'd told Ann Winter about, the strong fear of showing fear. And I couldn't really see myself as Clifford Hardy, MA, father of two and due for his long-service leave. I didn't need it. The fear was uncomfortable, but it suited me better to fight it than to give in to it.

The Commodore went faster in Chippendale as we headed up towards Anzac Parade. Bob flicked the wheel and we suddenly shot left down a one-way street. He went down a lane, turned and went back across Cleveland Street through a red light. He did another quick series of turns and I could see the lights of the Parade up ahead of us and the dark blankness of Moore Park off to the right.

'Lose 'em?' the smelly one asked.

Bob nodded and lit the cigarette he'd been carrying in his mouth the whole time.

That was the first thing to go wrong.

24

IT was Rushcutters Bay; the water slapped against the pier
and the boats and it was expensive water. Expensive to live
near and very expensive to sail on. It was cheap to swim in, but
the expensive boats' fuel and wastes had fixed it so no-one would
want to swim there. I thought of swimming as they herded me
through a concrete car park into a lift that ran up into the body
of a big apartment block. It was hard going without the stick
and with the knee brace and I lurched and grabbed at things
to steady myself. One-legged swimming would be no fun, especially with my hands tied. The guy who had a raw streak on
his face where the broken stick had hit him laughed when I fell
in the lift. I heaved myself up and wondered whether an off-
balance punch into the middle of his face would be worth what
I'd get in return. I decided it wouldn't.

We stepped out onto thick carpet and walked between creamy
walls with tasteful paintings economically spaced. At suite twelve
Bob knocked and brushed down his clothes. Sharon opened the
door. She was wearing a pink jump suit, was stilted up on four-
inch-heeled gold sandals and looked about sixteen, just. She
inclined her head, her platinum hair bounced and my escorts
bustled me down a short parqueted passage into a room with
thicker carpet than the hallway and worse paintings.

A man was sitting at a table in the middle of the room. The
table was covered with take-away food—cartons of chicken, two
medium-sized pizzas, Lebanese bread and meats and chipped
potatoes. He was eating with his fingers, stuffing the food in
and wiping his hands with a paper napkin. He was bulky, built
square and unmistakably the man who had parked his cadillac
outside Marion Singer's apartment building.

'Hello, Mac.' I said.

There was a nervous hiss of breath from Bob. Smelly sucked his teeth and went our of the room.

'Sit,' Mac said. 'Drink?' He was drinking beer from a pewter mug but there was a bar in the corner of the room under a painting of horses.

'Scotch.'

Mac combined more chewing with a nod and Sharon, who wasn't legally old enough to sniff the stuff, made the drink. She had a drink herself, something greenish. Bob wasn't invited to sit or drink, but he didn't seem to mind. I took the drink and made a close study of my host.

He was about five foot six, I guessed, and must have weighed sixteen stone. Some of the weight was in his belly, but most of it was meat and muscle packed high up on his chest, around his shoulders and into his thick neck. He had small blue eyes, a very high colour and silver hair brushed back. He had on a white business shirt with a light line in it, the dark trousers of an eight-hundred-dollar suit and black oxfords with a high gloss. He had no jewellery, no tie; white hair sprung out at the neck of the shirt. He looked about sixty and good for twenty more years if his eating habits changed.

'Why are you telling lies about me?' His voice was flat and neutral. He shook his head and spoke again before I could. 'Nothing but lies.' He gave the 'nothing' a touch of 'nothink'— a Christian Brothers boy, maybe.

I drank some of the scotch and rubbed my knee; my fingers slid over that disgusting plastic. 'I'm like that. I tell lies to find out the truth.'

Mac up-ended his pewter pot and held it out to Sharon, who was sipping her drink. I finished the scotch and stuck my glass out too.

'I don't want to talk to you,' Mac said. 'And I'm not giving you any more free drinks.' Sharon ignored me and took the pewter mug across to the bar, where she poured half a bottle of Cooper's ale into it. Mac ate some chips and took a big scoop of the hoummos up with a shovel of bread.

'I'm trying to find out what happened to John Singer.'

'He drowned.'

'Maybe.'

'Two years ago.'

'Maybe.'

He looked interested but not fascinated; his priorities at the moment seemed to be the food, the beer, Sharon and me. When she brought the beer over, she bent over and let him see down the front of her suit. I saw a bit too. I paired them mentally— with him on top you'd see her feet and forehead sticking out at either end. The idea amused me.

'I wouldn't smile if I was you, shithead,' Mac said. He took a big pull on the beer. 'Why're you going around saying Freddy Ward killed Singer and putting it on me?'

'Oh, that. I was just trying to stir things up. Actually, I think you probably killed him.'

'I thought you were a bullshitter when I first heard about you and now I know. Why would I kill John?'

'Ward's moving shop. With Singer gone, you'd control the game.'

He smiled around a big mouthful of pizza. I remembered that I was supposed to be trying to gauge his reactions, but it was hard with his face full of food. Also, I had the feeling that he was only half paying attention, that he was off on a tangent of some sort.

'Just like that?' he said.

'Well, you'd have to work things out with Marion.'

That ruffled him. His hand jerked and he almost spilled beer on his pants. 'You don't know her!' he spluttered. 'It's taken me . . .' He broke off and pushed his lower lip out under the upper in a 'what the hell' gesture. 'Well, that's no bloody business of yours. I didn't kill Singer. I don't think anyone killed him. There's nothink in it.'

'Why did you have me picked up, then?' I tried to put some aggression into the question, but I wasn't feeling at all aggressive. The session was very unsatisfactory. I was getting no change out of McLeary and all my experiment had got me so far was a broken walking stick.

150

I asked the question again, which only made me sound as nervous as I felt. I sneaked a look at Bob; he was leaning back against the wall, but not looking as bored as he should have been. Neither was Sharon; a little bit of tongue about the same colour as her suit was showing between her small, white teeth and her eyes were wide open and keen, as if she was watching something good on TV. Only Mac looked appropriately bored, and that could have been because he'd finished eating. He had a toothpick out and was excavating and sucking down the results. His baby blues were half closed and he seemed to be thinking. He dropped the toothpick into the remains of the hoummos and asked Sharon for a cigar. She got one from somewhere near the bar, brought it across and he lit it himself with a Dunhill lighter. He seemed to have forgotten my question. I felt very nervous and leaned forward to scratch my knee.

'Why do you do that?' Mac asked.

'It hurts.'

'Let's see it.'

I didn't move. Bob came up and touched me on the unbandaged ear with something hard and warm. It was the gun, which he must have been wearing somewhere nice and close to his armpit.

'Do you want him to pull his pants leg up, Mac, or should he drop them?'

Sharon sniggered and Mac gave a slight smile.

'Up,' he said. 'Don't want to excite Sharon too early in the night.'

The trousers weren't tight. I rolled the leg up past the knee to show the brace. In that comfortable atmosphere, composed of the food smells and the rich aroma of Mac's cigar, the device looked hideous. The plastic shone pink with a blue tint, like the skin of freshly cleaned rabbit. It was a reminder that flesh could be torn and bones broken.

Mac puffed out a billow of smoke. 'Nasty,' he said. 'Broken?'

I rolled the cloth back down. The cylinder was still inside the padding, but there didn't seem to be much point in sounding the alarm. I still didn't know what was going on in Mac's mind and for all I knew the cops could still have been circling the Nimrod Theatre. I could throw my glass and try for Bob's gun and the odds on that coming good were about the same as for Braddock beating Louis. It looked as if my only hope lay in some good talking. My tongue felt stiff and only half-linked to a sluggish brain.

'It's twisted,' I said. 'This guy in Bronte kicked me, and your offsider here broke my stick. Do you know Freddy Ward's heavy named Rex?'

'I know him,' Mac said.

'He's tougher than this bloke and I took him.'

'How was your leg then?' Bob asked.

'I'll look out for you when the leg gets better.'

It was thin stuff and not making any impression. The sweat of fear jumped out on me when I realised what an empty sound my last words had had. There was no response to them. The knee wasn't going to get better. Their faces wore the curious, dispassionate look of the judges at the Nuremberg trials. Wheels were in motion, inexorably.

Sharon spoke for the first time in a tinny, sick little voice. 'She might like that, the knee.' What she said made no sense to me, so I ignored it.

'I don't understand why you picked me up,' I said.

Mac waved his cigar hand expansively. 'You will, mate. Forget about Singer and all that. There's someone who wants to see you again.'

A door off to the right opened and Smelly came in with some sticking plaster across his face. He held the door wide and a smallish, dark figure glided into the room—Mary Mahoud.

25

MAHOUD didn't waste time getting down to business. One, two, three steps across the thick carpet in her desert boots and she was smashing me in the face with her fist. She had her arm back for the follow-up when Mac shook his silver head and said, 'Bob', quietly. It was a nice friendly name for a man in Bob's line of work, and I felt quite well-disposed towards him as he eased Mahoud away with a bit of arm and shoulder work.

'I wish I could say it was nice to see you,' I said.

She sneered at me. 'You'll be sorry for everything.' She wasn't panting with rage and her eyes weren't alight with triumph. They were dull, flat and malevolent. I gathered she blamed me for Manny's death and hadn't forgiven me for busting up her million-dollar gaol. It was a lot to hold against a man, and I had a feeling she had something unpleasant planned for me.

'You're crazy,' I said. 'You should be out of the country. Everyone's hunting you, Federal cops . . .'

'Manfred had all of that planned. A place to hide, but we thought we would have more time.'

'You grabbed the money and ran.'

She raised her hand as if she was going to hit me again. She had simple solutions. But she changed the movement into a shrug. 'Yes, I was afraid. I ran away.'

I understood her better then; she was feeling guilty about shooting through on Manfred and she'd never be able to justify it to him or herself. I was a good target for that disturbance, too. I turned to look at Mac and Sharon, but I made the movement a bit too suddenly and my dented head, torn ear and battered ribs all hurt.

'Do you know what this bitch did?' I said. 'She had these old people in cages like animals. She fed them cat food while she banked their pensions. She let them die; probably helped some of them along.'

'Probably,' Mac said. 'I read about it. No-hopers, plonkos, what do they matter? If the government's crazy enough to give people like that money, there'll be smarties around to take it off them.'

Sharon said, 'Cat food? I didn't read about that.'

'You can't read,' Mac said. 'It was on the telly, you should've seen it.'

'Ugh, cat food.'

'And pills and wine. They were zonked out most of the time.'

'Humane, I'd call it.' Mac gave his pot to Sharon again, patting her bum as she got up by way of apology for insulting her intelligence. Sharon swung her behind like a stripper on her way across to the bar. I'd been barking up the wrong tree trying to needle Mac. The talk had cheered him up; no-one was going to feed *him* cat food and cheap wine.

Mahoud got herself a tonic water and stayed near the window, sipping it. She didn't look as if she had come to much harm in the time that had passed since Manfred sent her off for the van. The bruise on the side of her face had faded and I realised how misleading my description of her had been. The light in the house of horrors and the whole context had led me to exaggerate her mean, foxy look but out in the street, wearing those androgynous clothes, nobody would take a second look at her. She certainly didn't look like a mass murderer. But then, neither had John Reginald Christie. One thing was certain, though; if she had any money on hand, she'd better watch it because I had the feeling that Mac around money was like a shark around offal. Maybe I could use that somehow. I moved the bad leg stiffly.

'What was that about his knee?' Mahoud asked.

'Badly twisted,' Bob said. 'He's got a sort of brace on it.'

Mahoud's face took on some some animation for the first time. 'Manny did that,' she said softly. 'I'd like to twist it back the other way.'

'Why not?' Bob said. Sharon seemed to like that; she tried to sip and laugh at the same time and a cough was the result.

'You're too young to drink,' I said.

'You shut up!' Mac snapped. 'There's a little package deal on here, Hardy, for your information. Miss Mahoud needs some documents which I can supply because she's got the do-re-mi. She's paid a bit more to meet up with you again. I was curious about you, too. My curiosity's satisfied.'

'Mine isn't,' I said. 'And the cops aren't far off. Bob only dropped some of them. They doubled up.'

'Crap!' Mac had his beer going down again and that always seemed to cheer him. 'That's garbage. You're shit scared, anyone could see that. The cops are so short-handed they shit in shifts. You dumped them, Bob. Right?'

'Right.'

'Good. Well, I'll be saying goodnight, Hardy. Bob and Terry can handle the rest of it, Miss Mahoud.'

She put her glass down hard. It made a ringing noise that swung every eye in the room her way.

'No, I don't trust them,' she said, fiercely. 'And I don't trust you. He might be telling the truth about the policemen. I want you there too, Mr Mac.'

'Listen,' Mac snarled. 'I don't do this sort of thing, not any more. You've got two good men and you've got my word.'

'No, you come or no money.'

Bob stepped up, but Mac signalled him back. Smelly Terry used the diversion to sneak himself a drink at the bar. Sharon glared at him, but Mac drank some more beer and appeared to be thinking. He wiped his mouth and got up. I read volumes in that, and none of it good for Mary Mahoud. 'All right,' Mac said heavily. 'You can come, too, Sharon.'

'No!' she squeaked. 'No, I don't want to.'

Mac slapped her twice. He swivelled to do it in the way wrestlers do, and he put some of that bulk into it. The girl staggered and he caught her.

'I don't want any unpleasantness, Sharon. Just do everythink you're told.'

He didn't include me in that. I was already beginning to feel that I wasn't there, wasn't anywhere.

'Where are we going?'

Mac grinned at me and looked across at Bob.

'I don't think the place has a name,' Bob said.

They bustled about collecting car keys and cigarettes, like people getting ready for a picnic. Terry picked up a slice of pizza and tucked it away. Mac looked at him indulgently; Terry was evidently going to come into his own soon, and I doubted that his speciality was bird calls.

We made quite a crowd in the lift. Sharon edged away from Terry for obvious reasons, but no-one else seemed to mind his lack of personal freshness. Bob carried himself admirably—loose and unencumbered, leaving himself plenty of space to do whatever was called for. Mac was grim-faced, Mahoud looked edgy and I had to concentrate on keeping upright.

Terry scouted the car park and gave Bob the high sign. Mac handed Terry his keys.

'Get the Merc over here,' he said.

Then there was a shout and two shots and bodies were moving apart as if a great, sharp blade was slashing at them. I dived for the ground, the knee screaming as I went. An interior light in a car positioned near the Commodore flashed on and I saw Freddy Ward's arm jerk up. There was a shot from behind and above me—I guessed from Bob—and the windscreen of Ward's car was starred. Two rapid shots came from another direction and there was a grunt behind me. I thought I might as well make my contribution and I scrabbled at my trouser leg. Someone shouted 'Stop!' There was another shot and then echoes and then silence.

A voice, close to my ear asked, 'What are you doing, Cliff?'

I let go of my pants, swore and turned my head to see Roger Wallace of the Wallace Brown Agency. He stands about six foot four in his three-piece suit.

'Hello, Rog,' I croaked. 'You're not supposed to be here.'

'Word gets around, Cliff. When Freddy got out the guns and came after Mac, I knew you'd be in the middle. You owe me money; I had to take steps to protect it.'

'I'm glad you did. Who shot who?'

He helped me up and I leaned against a Rover which felt solid enough to prop me up.

'Let's see.' He lifted his head and looked across the neon-lit concrete. 'Ward shot one of McLeary's boys. He's dead. One of my boys shot a guy in Ward's car. He's not dead.'

Freddy Ward and another man were standing by the car with the broken windscreen. One of Roger's operatives was covering them a bit dramatically with a pistol. Ward looked pale and gaunt under the light. I blew him a kiss and his face went stony. I couldn't see Rex or Tal. Behind me Terry was standing stock still near the lift, his hands reaching up for the illuminated sign that said 'Elevator'. Another of Roger's men was watching him but dividing his attention between Terry and a huddle on the ground that was bright and dark and making sobbing noises.

I limped over and saw that it was Mac with his head in Sharon's lap. I looked at Roger and he shook his head.

'Not shot. Heart, I think. Ambulance on the way.'

Bob's legs were sticking out from behind a car. Those big bullets push hard.

'Did you see a dark woman with us, Roger?'

'Quickest mover I ever saw. She took off.' He pulled out a packet of Marlboro and offered them. I put out my hand, remembered, and pulled it back. I shook my head and other parts of me were shaking as well.

'Cliff,' Roger blew a stream of smoke in Terry's direction. 'What were you doing with your strides down there on the ground?'

'It's going to rain,' I said. 'I was scratching my knee.'

26

THE cops had never had so many licensed, bonded private detectives together in the one place at the one time before, and they made the most of it. The scene at Police Headquarters was like something out of *Colombo* and the cops swaggered or bumbled around, according to how they cast themselves. Roger Wallace got through it all with an icy smile on his face. His men frazzled a little towards the end and I frazzled a lot as my leg hurt me more and more. Analgesics and caffeine were fighting skirmishes in my system, bombing and strafing and laying waste to the territory. Roger's men mocked me for not having a gun, but I couldn't see that they needed any more guns. Frank Parker and I had an unspoken pact—he wouldn't draw attention to my bleeper if I wouldn't mention how easily the late Bob had dropped his men off in Redfern.

Frederick Allan Ward was charged with murder, which would be reduced to manslaughter because he had a good enough lawyer to see to that. A policewoman took Sharon off somewhere, I never found out where. Rex and Bob were dead, Mac was in hospital and Terry was charged with silly stuff like unlicensed firearms and attempted abduction.

Before everything wound up about three am, the news came through that Mac had died of a massive coronary. In the taxi on the way home I reflected that Freddy Ward's chances of becoming the vice king of Macarthur Onslow land had taken a nosedive. That left Mrs Marion Singer. I thought about her just a little.

I went to sleep on the couch at four am, fell off it an hour and a half later and couldn't get back to sleep. I made coffee as the sun came up, and my crashing about in the kitchen woke Hilde, who came down the stairs yawning and rubbing her eyes.

Her hair was all tousled and she had a warm bed smell. She pulled her dressing-gown tight. We drank the coffee sitting on the couch; my clothes were lying around on the floor and the leg brace draped across a chair looked like a cross between a jockstrap and a groin shield. I had a black, gravelly beard and sour breath. She finished her coffee first and did a quick, professional examination of my knee.

'Sore?'

'Bloody sore.'

'Well, what happened to Michael Caine?'

'I don't know.'

'You *still* don't know? But I got the impression your job was finished.'

'I think it is. I think my client's entirely satisfied and I've lost enough skin and sleep over the bloody thing, anyway.'

That day the hospital bill came and I sent it to Mrs Singer. I used the knee exerciser. I limped into town and bought a new walking stick with a rubber tip and a nice swing to it. My patience gave out that evening and I tried to phone Mrs Singer, but there was no answer. She called me the next day. I heard STD bleeps and an urgent note in her voice.

'I want you to come up here, Mr Hardy. I'm at my place on the Hawkesbury.'

'That's nice, Mrs Singer. Can't you just tell me all about it on the phone? I've got a few accounts to send you, of course.'

'No, no. I have something to show you and we have a lot to talk about.'

'I take it you're satisfied.'

She paused. 'All your expenses will be met in full. I really *must* see you. As far as I'm concerned, I'm still employing you.'

That surprised me. I didn't exactly mind being paid for sitting around resting my leg, reading a bit and having a quiet drink or two, but it added to my confusion. I tried to draw her out on how my erratic activities had pleased her, but she wouldn't play. She asked me to have lunch with her at the Beleura Waters restaurant on the river. When I hesitated, she suggested that the invitation was an order.

159

'I can't drive with this knee.'

'I'll send a car.'

What could I say? A Fairlane with a taciturn Scot at the wheel arrived at eleven am and we set off north.

He didn't talk well, but he was a terrific driver. We moved smartly against the sluggish flow of traffic down into the narrow streets of Sydney. We got to the river about midday, parked, and I waited for the restaurant boat to pick me up.

'What'll you do?' I asked the driver.

'I'll wait,' he said. 'I have a packed lunch.'

It was a bright, warm day. Spring comes to the Hawkesbury. There were patches of green and yellow on the rocky river banks where grass and wildflowers had gained a hold. The trees were aggressively native, gums that exhibited all the shades from khaki to grey. But we loved them. The other revellers numbered about half a dozen and included a state cabinet minister. Parliament was sitting that day as far as I knew, but the minister had a very pretty young Asian woman with him, so I suppose he could have been on a goodwill mission. I had on my best drill slacks and a denim shirt that I'd ironed. I also had my new walking stick and the bandage was off my ear.

The boat was a wide, flat-bottomed craft with a fringed awning over the seating section and a convincing Johnson outboard motor. A thin, elegant boatman handed us in and whipped the boat out into the current.

Half the people in the boat didn't need lunch and the rest looked like professional dieters. The minister kept his hand on the Asian woman's knee and looked into her almond eyes. I was glad I wasn't driving. The restaurant had a reputation for drinkable wine.

The restaurant is a plain brick and stone affair set right on the river. It has a couple of hundred square feet of unfashionable louvre windows that should look terrible but don't.

Mrs Singer was waiting for us at a corner table commanding the best view of the river. She was dressed to kill in a white linen suit. Her silvery hair had that expensive disarray and her makeup was somewhere between bold and restrained. Up close, there were signs of strain around her eyes and mouth, but she put together a pretty good smile.

'Mr Hardy,' she said. 'That stick and limp are maddeningly attractive.'

'They look better than they feel, Mrs Singer.'

'Marion,' she said. 'What will you drink?'

'Gin and tonic, thanks, like before.'

'Being bashed hasn't affected your memory. I'm sorry you had such a hard time.'

She looked concerned, but not sorry.

The drinks came. She seemed determined to stay off business for a while, and I let her. She was laying on the charm and affluence with a trowel and there had to be a reason. The menu arrived and we chatted about that. She had a medallion of venison and a lettuce leaf. I had a steak. She ordered a bottle of German wine, most of which I drank while she sipped Perrier. She pointed out a few local characters as boats puttered by on the river. I noticed that she'd upped her tar content—she was smoking Rothmans and plenty of them.

No sweets by consensus; on to coffee and down to business. Marion hauled out her cheque book and wrote out a big one for days worked, expenses incurred and some for luck. Lots for luck.

'Thanks,' I said. 'Lovely lunch, too. Now, tell me how I earned it.'

The strain was showing more clearly now; there were tiny lines running down into that superbly defined mouth and her eyes had unhappy depths. She took a couple of sheets of paper from her handbag and passed them to me. A waiter came with cigars. I thought for a second, *Why not?* and then I thought, *Why?*

The sheets were typed on and numbered. The first carried a date two years and a few weeks before.

Darling Marion,

No easy way to say it. I've got cancer, It's bad and there's no stopping it. They told me in the States that I've got a few months to go at the most. So I've made some arrangements and there are a few things you have to do if you want to hang on to everything we've built up. First, I've got some stuff to take that will finish me. I'm going to take it in the water as far out as I can get. It won't be too bad. Lyle Robinson has the will and it's watertight. You can trust him with the legal stuff. You can't trust anyone else, so do as I say.

Ward and Mac will try to take over. Mac will try hardest. They'll wait a while, maybe a year or so until the casino deal runs out but Mac will have a go. Stall him.

You're going to need a stirrer. Rhino Jackson could do it and you know him. But he's a drunk. Ron Clingan is tough enough and pretty smart. He'd do. The best would be this private detective named Cliff Hardy. He's ex-army, which is a plus. He's pretty hard and he sticks. But he's not dumb, so you have to be careful. When Mac gets difficult you should contact this Hardy and tell him some story about me still being alive. You'll have to put on a good act. Get him working on it. Pay him what he asks, but no more. Keep him keen. Don't tell him about Mac and Ward, he'll find out and make trouble for them. The word on him is that he keeps going until he gets there. He'll scare the shit out of Ward, who wants to get out of stuff here as you know. But he's got that terrible temper. Mac isn't that bright and he's got a crook heart, I found out. This Hardy should be able to push them into doing something silly and get them in so much trouble they'll be off your back.

Your one problem is that Hardy could get himself killed between now and when you need him. If that happens, be patient and get the best man you can for the job. I thought of killing Freddy and Mac myself but I wouldn't get both of them, and it could make a lot of trouble for you.

So do it this way, love. It was all great with you, lots of fun and no-one really ever mattered to me except you. I want it to go on for you. I had to pull out a lot of cash to cover some things and people, but you hang on to the rest.

Goodbye, Marion

The signature was a bold scrawl: 'John'.

I read it carefully, and read parts of it twice. Marion Singer got another Rothmans going; her eyes were wet and a muscle was jumping out of control on the left side of her face.

'Well, it worked,' I said.

'Yes.' She blew smoke awkwardly. 'He was just the smartest man I ever knew. It worked perfectly.'

I remembered that Sandy Modesto, one of the ones who never really mattered, had used almost the same words about Singer.

'But . . .?' I said.

The hand holding the cigarette was shaking, and she looked every one of her fifty-plus years. 'You won't believe this. I can hardly believe it myself. But I've been told that John is in Bangkok. He was seen. He's had plastic surgery. There's a girl . . . Shit!'

She smashed out the cigarette. The ashtray hopped and sprayed ash and spent matches over her white suit. I grinned.

'Don't look like that! Hardy, don't! I must know! I'll pay you anything you ask to go to Bangkok. I'll pay you fifty thousand dollars.'

'No,' I said.